TASTE THE SWEET REBELLION

REBEL AGAINST DIETING

WORKBOOK

REBEL DIETITIANS®

KAIT FORTUNATO RD, LD • **DANA MAGEE RD, LD, CLT**

REBECCA BITZER MS, RD, LD, CEDRD

Taste the Sweet REBELLION

REBEL Against Diets Workbook

by Kait Fortunato Greenberg, Dana Magee, and Rebecca Bitzer

Published by Empowered Enterprises

© 2015 by Kait Fortunato Greenberg, Dana Magee, and Rebecca Bitzer. All rights reserved.

Books may be purchased by contacting the author at:

Rebecca Bitzer MS, RD & Associates
7219 D Hanover Parkway
Greenbelt, MD 20770
301-474-2499
admin@empoweredeatingblog.com

Cover Design: Summer Morris, Sumo Design Studio
Interior Design: Jennifer Ditzig and Clara Flynn
Editor: Julie Beyer, MA, RDN
ISBN: 978-0-9904010-1-8

REBEL Dietitian® is a registered trademark of Rebecca Bitzer MS, RD & Associates

Printed in the United States of America

DEDICATION

*Dedicated to our courageous clients and those
recovering from dieting hardships.*

*Remember you did not fail, but the diet was set up
to fail you from the very beginning.*

*May you help to spread the message that food can
be both nutritious and enjoyable for every BODY.*

CONTENTS

ACKNOWLEDGEMENTS

We would like to thank the many people who offered assistance, inspiration, and support during the preparation and execution of this workbook.

Thank you to our dietetic student interns both past and present who believe in the REBEL approach and continue to spread our message.

Thank you *Mollie Spiesman* for being our REBEL research assistant. Thank you for your dedication, efficiency, and communication throughout this project.

Thank you *Alex Raymond* and *Klara Knezevic* for joining us on a snowy writing retreat to help make this workbook full of fun and inspiration.

Thank you to our families who believed in us and supported us every step of the way. We are sure you had no idea how much time and energy we would put into this workbook and how much you would be involved in the process. We are very grateful for your support.

Thank you to all the REBEL-minded health professionals who came before us who believe in the non-dieting approach and help people everywhere feel inspired and empowered.

Thank you to our editor, *Julie Beyer, MA, RDN*, for helping us clarify our writing and for helping us spread our message.

Thank you to our returning cover designer, *Summer Morris*, for delivering a cover that brings our thoughts and ideas to life.

Thank you *Jennifer Ditzig* and *Clara Flynn* for creating images that capture the content and REBEL feel of our work, helping us convey our message in a fun and interesting way.

Thank you *Millie Plotkin* for your help in hunting down staggering dieting statistics which truly stand out in this workbook.

FINALLY...

Thank you to each other for making this writing experience so memorable and fun. We wove our strengths together to make this workbook so much more than it would have been if we had done it alone.

Kait, you have unbelievable focus, determination, and an endless ability to concentrate which helped us get this workbook done in record time.

Dana, you have an incredible spirit and enthusiasm that keeps us energized through the challenges of actually putting our thoughts and ideas into written words.

Rebecca, thank you for instilling in us the entire basis on which this workbook was built. Thank you for showing us how to nurture our clients' happiness and health without dieting.

INTRODUCTION

Your REBEL Dietitians® cordially invite you to join the REBELLION. It is time to take a stand and change the conversation around the dinner table to that of body empowerment and positive discussions about food. As REBELs, our goal is to bring the joy back to eating while leaving dieting behind.

You picked up this book wanting something different; we are here to help you in an entirely new way.

Are you sick and tired of dieting? Are you ready to REBEL?

We are REBELs—smashing the scale, ditching the diets, and embracing what is truly important in life.

In this workbook, you will see how diets are doomed to fail and how the most current nutrition research brings hope to help you find health and happiness without dieting. We have examined and digested the huge body of scientifically proven nutrition research and want to share this knowledge with you in a fun, REBELLIOUS way. We didn't invent the non-dieting approach, but we have embraced it with thousands of our clients. You will notice quotes throughout the workbook from many leaders in the fields of nutrition and psychology.

> Science supports the value of the non-dieting approach. As published in the leading nutrition resource, *The Journal of the Academy of Nutrition and Dietetics*, interventions that encourage intuitive eating (eating in accordance with internal cues of hunger and fullness), decrease unhealthy eating behaviors (such as dietary restraint and binge eating), signifying a healthier relationship with food. Researchers also identified improvements in blood pressure, blood lipid levels, and cardiorespiratory fitness. Furthermore, intuitive eating programs decrease depression and anxiety, increase self-esteem, and improve body image. (We will discuss more about intuitive eating in Chapter 3.)
>
> Schaefer J, Magnunson A. A review of interventions that promote eating by internal cues. *Journal of the Academy of Nutrition and Dietetics*. 2014; 114(5): 634-760.

You will also discover many ways to REBEL against diets, improve your mental and physical health, and ultimately ***Taste the Sweet REBELLION***. We hope you enjoy our fun, practical way to change your relationship with food while empowering your life with our REBELLIOUS spin.

In the pages that follow, you will address **what**, **where**, **when**, **why**, and **how** you are eating. This will be unlike any "diet" book you have ever picked up. We are not trying to sell you on our food, our calorie counting site, our measuring cups, our supplements, or anything else you may find in the typical diet plans these days. The goal of this workbook is for you to find awareness in your eating habits and to target and improve your nutrition behaviors. By embracing the REBEL approach, you will learn more about yourself, nourish your mind and body, feel healthier, and address your weight concerns.

What Is REBEL?

REBEL stands for:

R = RESIST Diets
E = EAT Like a REBEL
B = BUILD Confidence in Your Eating
E = EMPOWER Yourself
L = LIVE Joyfully

The REBEL approach got its name after we observed the same scenario unfolding over and over again. We were bearing witness to the same negative impact that diets were having on our clients mentally, physically, and emotionally. While the main goal was to live a healthier, more joyful life, we saw dieting create more stress, more guilt, AND the weight was returning. The truth behind conventional dieting is that it can be restrictive, keeping you from enjoying the food you love. Diets are often difficult to maintain, not to mention the stress of adhering to the plan or the guilt you feel if you fall off the wagon. Many people see weight loss at first, but inevitably find the weight comes back.

Using the REBEL approach means you feel comfortable incorporating the foods you love as well as reducing the stress of feeding yourself and your family. We decided to start a REBELLION and encourage clients to REBEL against the dieting culture and not to allow our society's narrow perception of beauty to dictate happiness. As REBEL Dietitians®, we feel nutrition is very important, but it is not the only key to happiness and only deserves a small space in your everyday life. We can help you put food back in its place, leaving you room to invest in your relationships, engage in self-care, and embrace what truly matters. Using the non-dieting approach, this workbook will provide you with the tools you need to be successful, improving your happiness and health. For more support we encourage you to connect with your REBEL Dietitians® and a community of REBELS using our Facebook page: *Taste the Sweet REBELLION* (https://www.facebook.com/REBELdiets).

Meet REBEL Client "Julie"

Julie struggled with her weight and had been a lifelong dieter when we met. She was an encyclopedia of dieting information—an expert on calories, points, rules, and restrictions. I could see the look of defeat and worry on her face as she prepared to embark on what she thought would be another strict program to follow.

"The more I know about you and your life, the more I can help you," I said, "I want to hear your story." Shocked that I did not first ask about what she was doing "wrong," Julie began telling me about herself.

I learned Julie worked long hours and was often the "go-to" person at work, taking the brunt of the responsibilities. Her co-workers expected her to have all of the answers. In an attempt to please everyone, she did not prioritize breaks for meals, often eating only once a day. Her relationship with food deteriorated further when she moved to a new location across the country, inducing stress eating at night. Julie felt isolated. Feelings of loneliness started her on a cycle of emotionally eating, yet she avoided social events because she felt shameful about her weight. Do parts of Julie's story sound familiar to you?

Using the REBEL approach, Julie was able to prioritize her meals and employ quick meal and snack ideas that fit into her busy schedule. She collected an array of easy recipes to implement at home, and she developed confidence when eating out. Her next step was to look past the food and work on acceptance and self-care. Julie not only improved her health, but she was meeting new people at work and becoming more social as she joined others for happy hours and brunches. She was confident in ordering what she wanted without feeling guilty. She found her inner REBEL and no longer allowed her insecurities about her weight to dictate her life. It was inspiring to see Julie's mindset shift from focusing solely on weight loss to embracing a full and meaningful life free of diets.

Like many of our clients, Julie did lose weight as she built REBEL skills including improving her nutrition, prioritizing self-care, and being more mindful. She was finally able to lay down the burden of dieting. Julie still checks in to help keep her health and nutrition a priority throughout life's stressful ups and downs.

Julie got a *Taste of the Sweet REBELLION*.

Are you ready to take a bite?

SELF-ASSESSMENT

In order to reap the full benefits of this workbook, we will periodically encourage you to reflect on, brainstorm, and explore many aspects of your nutrition, health, body image, and quality of life. Before digging in, please take the time to fill out this self-assessment to learn more about yourself and your journey. If you are working with a registered dietitian, we suggest you share this with them. We encourage you to answer openly, honestly, and without judgment to get the most out of this workbook.

1. Describe your weight history from the time you were born:

   I was born in 1947 at the end of WW II. Following the war folks were more concerned about the prospect of fat not dieting. I was like little Shirley Temple... healthy not thin at all. I was expected to be big not obese but full hipped and short like my grandmother. Eating was and is ritual, tradition, a celebration. I am not actually great friends with folks I can not share a meal.

2. How much of your life energy is going into fears related to your weight, thinking about food, the number on the scale, or counting calories?

   (none at all)   1 2 3 4 5 6 7 8 ⑨ 10   (all consuming)

3. If you could wave a magic wand, what would you like your health and eating habits to look like (stop calorie counting, stop binging, stop gaining weight) to be in the next:

   a. Three months

      Become aware of my triggers and listing meal plans. Develop the habit of exercising with friends and family.

   b. Six months

      Become a quiet storm, a rebel, determined to be my own advocate for health... an overcomer.

   c. One year

      A strong, serene, and sexy seventy year old weighing in at a healthy, happy 160 lbs.

4. What do you think is slowing you down, standing in your way, or stopping you from meeting these goals?

I do not want to succeed at my health goals because I will gain more attention and at times I want to be invisible; on the other hand I'm competitive and want to win

5. Describe your dieting history:

In my 20's I was not more than 135 lbs. I did not think about weight. Birth Control pills increased my weight which started the cycle of gain/loss after birth #1. Got back to 135 lbs. after birth #2 until a hysterectomy at 40 yrs. Struggled through the 40's with Weight Watchers, Nutrisystem etc., etc. hooked amag, at 50 yrs. Retired at 55 yrs. Planned many things. Then became caregiver and padded my body to offset verbal, emotional abuse.

6. How often do you weigh yourself?

Not at all now, but I intend to weigh again.

7. What do people close to you think about your eating and weight?

_____
_____

8. Do you feel pressure from your family, friends, and health professionals to lose weight?

Yes, pressure from light to heavy.
_____

9. In what ways has dieting put your life on hold, preventing you from doing the things you love?

_____
_____

10. What do you hope to get out of this workbook?

information, inspiration, and a last ditch inclination to change, to heal myself...
_____
_____
_____

5

The REBEL Manifesto

Our philosophy on resisting diets while nourishing your mind, body, and soul.

1. **RESIST** diets and boldly nourish your mind and body. This includes working through this workbook to learn the skills needed to fuel your body while resisting ALL diets and food rules. NO more "good vs. bad" foods.
2. **EAT** like a REBEL by embracing nutrition and learning how to nourish your body like a pro. Nutrition knowledge is power. Embrace science-based nutrition facts and avoid harmful, trendy, sensationalized nutrition information. It means eating with nutrition principles in mind while enjoying a wide variety of foods. Eating like a REBEL means connecting with your mind, body, and soul in order to fine-tune your nutrition to meet your individual needs.
3. **BUILD** confidence in your eating by increasing your awareness on **when**, **why**, **where**, and **how** you eat. Learn to trust your hunger and practice *savoring* your food. It means developing skills to stop using food to smother or distract from your emotions and understanding the difference between physical hunger and emotional hunger by closely listening to your body.
4. **EMPOWER** yourself by building a healthy relationship with food and developing a healthy relationship with your body. Set up your environment for success, and give yourself permission to practice self-care including making mindful food choices, embracing movement for joy, and practicing gratitude in daily life.
5. **LIVE** joyfully by unleashing your inner REBEL, ceasing comparisons, appreciating your body as it is today, divorcing the dieting industry, and ditching diets forever.

Break out of dieting prison and stay out. Embrace what is truly important in your life!

RESIST DIETS
EAT LIKE A REBEL
BUILD CONFIDENCE IN EATING
EMPOWER YOURSELF
LIVE JOYFULLY

CHAPTER 1: Resist Diets

"Diets are all or nothing. Life isn't." Michelle May, MD
Eat What You Love, Love What You Eat

A New Life Awaits

Improving nutrition has more to do with your health than with weight. As you fine-tune your eating habits and limit stress around food, you will also improve your overall quality of life. To the 75 million people who are on a diet in the United States every day, we are here to offer you another option, another way of life. This workbook will supply you with the necessary tools to resist the diet mentality, allow yourself to enjoy food, learn how to nourish your body, identify your individual hunger cues, and live a life according to what you value most.

Are You in Diet Prison?

You may never have thought about dieting as having a negative impact on your life. You may still be seeing it as the solution; however, we are here to shed some light on how this can become a vicious cycle and may actually be pulling you further from your health and nutrition goals. Throughout this workbook, we will be referring to the diet-after-diet cycle as "diet prison," an illustration describing the restrictive traps that dieting places on nutrition and enjoyment of food. Are you in "diet prison"? Ask yourself these questions:

- *Have you ever avoided going out to dinner with friends because the restaurant did not have options to support your current diet?* no
- *Have you ever gone to bed hungry in order to follow the "No eating after 8 p.m." rule?* yes
- *Have you ever missed having ice cream with your friends or family because of your "dairy-free" diet?* no
- *Have you ever denied yourself cake at a birthday party or wedding you attended?* no
- *Have you ever felt overwhelmed by calorie counting, strict dieting rules, or lists of "forbidden" foods?* Yes !!!

Now, you may wonder how you got into this diet prison. We want you to know it is not your fault and there is a way out. The goal of this workbook is to provide you with the insight and skills you need to stay out of diet prison for the rest of your life.

It's time to unleash your inner REBEL and break free from the dieting prison. So let's look at the life cycle of a diet to understand its downfalls. Dieting might seem healthy, but it is actually a predictable chain of events that often leads to disaster. These events include the trigger, the allure, the restriction, and the guilt.

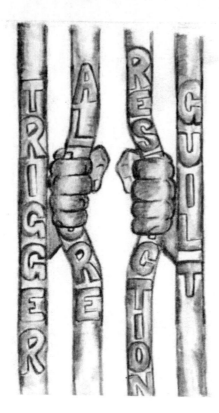

The Trigger: Every diet begins with some sort of negative feeling. We've listed common feelings below that may lead to dieting. Some people are able to weather these triggers like a Teflon® pan, and these feelings slide right off, whereas some are more like Velcro®. These triggers stick and are internalized, cultivating feelings of shame and diminishing self-worth:

- **Feeling insecure:** You feel compelled to begin dieting as a means to change your body shape, size, or weight. You believe the diet will make your life better.
- **Feeling out of control:** When life feels out of control, you often grasp onto something such as a diet. This can give you the perceived feeling of being in control while putting other problems on hold.
- **Feeling pressured:** Society and media play a huge part in determining what body types and foods are "acceptable," causing you to jump into a diet that will help you assimilate into the dieting culture. This pressure may come from the media's obsession with the way certain body parts *should* look such as the trending "thigh-gap" or "bikini-bridge."
- **Feeling scared:** You worry about your family medical history or your own new medical diagnosis, throwing you into a diet and believing it will reverse all of your health concerns.

What are your most common dieting triggers?

_____

_____

_____

The Allure: Unfortunately, once your trigger has made you vulnerable, it is understandable that you want to look for a solution. Because we live in a dieting culture, you don't have to look far to be "allured" by a diet. Most diets start with an exciting promise which sounds too good to be true. If it sounds too good to be true, it probably is. Understanding more about the allure of dieting will help you resist diets and the impractical claims that come along with them. How many times have you heard promises like the following?

- *"Lose 30 pounds in 30 days!"*
- *"Lose weight with our miracle diet patch or cream!"*
- *"Miracle fat-burner in a bottle!"*

These claims can be very enticing! The dieting industry will tell you that you need a certain product to be beautiful, healthy, and happy. They not only promise that you will lose weight, but you will get into a new relationship, go on vacation, and get a better job. If you could only lose weight with this product, you will have all you ever wanted, insinuating that it is the extra weight that is holding you back. What the diet industry doesn't disclose are the negative effects that dieting will have on your mental, physical, and emotional health.

What false promises have diets made to you in the past?

That their plan whatever it may be will fit my uniquely creative individual self and will work for my entire life. Any failure of their amazing program is solely my fault

The Restriction: *"Avoid foods that are 'bad' even if they are foods you love."* One thing that diets have in common is restrictions placed on food. The details change with each diet, but they all focus on some kind of food avoidance. Many diets begin with the elimination of an entire food category such as starches, dairy, or animal products. Yet, all of these foods supply essential nutrients. Even if you are balancing all of the food categories, you are still at risk for the physical and mental stressors of dieting if you are not eating enough.

These food restrictions often become a slippery slope. You start by avoiding a few foods, but tend to add to your "bad food" list over time. This can leave you with a very short list of "diet-approved" foods, making eating both boring and frustrating as you try to plan meals with limited options.

Restricting your diet can threaten your mental health and may cause:

- ☑ Lethargy
- ☑ Inability to focus
- ☑ Depression
- ☑ Irritability
- ☐ Isolation
- ☑ Constant thoughts of food
- ☑ Memory loss

Other physical effects that you might experience after prolonged dietary restriction include:

- ☐ Hair loss
- ☐ Brittle nails
- ☑ Constipation
- ☑ Fatigue
- ☑ Nausea
- ☑ Diarrhea
- ☑ Sexual dysfunction

Review the lists above and check off any side effects that you have experienced in the past when dieting.

The Guilt: There is an overwhelming sense of guilt once you fall off a diet plan. In your mind, you have failed. You can forget about promises of a happy future. Guilt is the next step of the dieting cycle—in the end, you feel terrible about yourself and think, "It's my own fault; I don't have the willpower to follow this simple diet." As a result, you go back to old habits, overeat from restricting food for so long, and gain back whatever weight was lost (if any). The feeling of failure overwhelms you until another triggering force hits, and the cycle starts all over.

Letter from Diet Prison

REBEL Dietitians,

I am MAD that so much of my life energy has been consumed by dieting. I am MAD that despite all of this I am not slim. This is my fault. I feel hopeless, I am not sure what to do next.

-Dieting Darla

POST CARD
Food Police Dept.

PLACE STAMP HERE

Rebel Dietitians
7219 Hanover Pikway
Suite D
Greenbelt, MD
20770

As REBEL Dietitians®, we are here to help you stop feeling guilty, and we solemnly swear to never to be the "food police," casting judgment on your food choices or preferences. We are here to explain the scientific research of dieting, show how diets are the problem, and how they are set up to fail you, not the other way around.

Resist the diets; ditch the guilt!

How do you feel when you are not successful on a diet? How has this affected the way you see yourself?

Guilt and more as a people pleaser, I transfer parental pleasing to the Dietian... I see myself as inauthentic, unable to follow through.

The Dark Side of Dieting

Our viewpoint may be somewhat controversial, considering about 55% of adults in the United States are currently on a diet. So, if over half of the adults in the United States are dieting, why are two-thirds of adults overweight or obese (as classified by the body mass index or BMI)?

Since research shows that dieting does not work for 95% of people, we think we can handle the criticism from the remaining 5% for whom restrictive dieting "worked." You

> ### Dieting Quick Facts
>
> **55%** of adults in the US are on a diet right now.
>
> **60.9** *billion* dollars are spent on diet products each year
>
> **95%** of weight lost through dieting is regained in 2 to 5 years.
>
>
>
> *"Dieting…may in part be responsible for the current obesity epidemic."* (Pietilainen, 2011)

may even think that one diet or another worked for you, but if that is so, why didn't it sustain your weight loss? Something led you to this book. You know intuitively that there is more to nutrition and weight management than you have experienced in previous attempts to diet. Now is the time to trust your intuition and open yourself to something new!

"You haven't failed your diet; your diet has failed you." Judith Matz, LCSW and Ellen Frankel, LCSW
The Diet Survivors Handbook: 60 Lessons in Eating, Acceptance, and Self-Care

The Dieting Culture Is Fueled by Diet Marketing

Our culture is saturated with diet marketing! The media constantly bombards us with new diet plans, pills, and cleanses that all sound promising and convincing. We are exposed to $180 million in diet and weight management advertising each year!

The dieting industry uses a variety of platforms to reach you—the Internet, magazines, television, billboards, and even your own acquaintances, friends, and family members. Unfortunately, the media's influence shapes society's view of what is normal, beautiful, and valued, starting from the time you were young. They perpetuate the idea that thin is ideal by any means necessary.

The allure of diets is especially strong when you are feeling vulnerable about your body. You begin to believe you are not good enough, that the weight is your fault, and that you would be ten times happier if you could just lose a little weight. However, in our experience, if you do not care for yourself and start to accept the person you are, regardless of your size, you will continue to fall short of happiness. Diets never start with a positive attitude; rather, they start with a photo that makes you feel like you look larger than you thought, an off-putting comment, or a comparison with a friend or family member. During the diet, depriving yourself of favorite foods and inadequate nutrition continues to wear on your mental health and body image, contributing to a cycle that is hard to break.

The Body Is Designed to Survive

Dieting stimulates the body's natural survival mechanisms by:

- Increasing cravings

- Decreasing metabolism

- Reducing muscle mass

- Increasing android fat (the fat around the midsection) due to weight cycling

---

You might be thinking, "*But, I went on a diet and I did lose weight!*" We are not denying that these diets sometimes cause weight loss, but maintaining that loss is unrealistic. In fact, approximately 95% of weight lost through dieting is regained within two to five years. Because the body does not like rapid weight loss, it protects itself by increasing appetite and craving rich, calorie-dense foods. After the initial loss, the body holds onto fat and calories, and weight loss slows or stops. This plateau is frustrating, and the dieter feels as though he or she failed. In 31 long-term studies on the effectiveness of dieting, it was concluded that dieting was a consistent predictor of weight gain—up to two-thirds of the people regained more weight than they lost. The number of diets an individual has tried is positively correlated with weight gain.

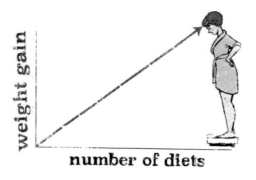

"If diets work, why do we go on them every year?" Julie Duffy Dillon, RD, LD, CEDRD

The nature of diets is that you are either "on a diet" or "off a diet," setting you up for failure from the beginning. What happens the moment you go "off a diet?" You go back to the old, familiar eating habits. Then, with the addition of each diet, the confusion and conflicting viewpoints deteriorate these habits even further. Before you know it, a tempting promise of rapid weight loss draws you right back into the dieting prison. The dieting cycle continues.

Just Say NO to Diets

You may have heard people say that while drugs, alcohol, and tobacco addictions can be treated with avoidance, food issues cannot be treated with abstinence. However, there is a similarity in that some people can experiment with drugs or alcohol and move on while others become stuck in the throes of abuse. For some people, dieting can be the gateway to a full-fledged eating disorder. For example, two young women who decide to go on a diet together may have very different experiences. One may be on the diet for a few days or weeks, and then she is off the diet never giving it another thought. Her dieting partner, however, may have a genetic predisposition that turns dieting into an obsession about food and calories, potentially evolving into an eating disorder. It may surprise you to learn that the risk of developing an eating disorder is more than 50% genetic. Thus, the restriction of dieting, combined with the genetic predisposition, can lead to anorexia nervosa, bulimia nervosa, binge eating disorder, or a combination of all three. Eating disorders are serious illnesses with life-threatening physical and psychological complications. Ask yourself these questions:

- *Do you sometimes feel that you have lost control over your eating?* never had control
- *Do you feel as though you are addicted to food?* yes
- *Are you struggling with binge eating disorder (BED)?* no

Binge eating disorder

In 2014, the medical community recognized BED as an eating disorder. BED is real, and we know you may be suffering. We are here to help you gain freedom from your food struggles and help you look at food in a completely different way to keep you from becoming a career criminal in dieting prison.

Binge eating disorder is defined as recurrent and persistent episodes of binge eating. Binge eating episodes are associated with three or more of the following:

- Eating until feeling uncomfortably full
- Eating large amounts of food when not hungry
- Eating alone because of embarrassment
- Feeling disgusted with yourself; feeling depressed or guilty
- Marked distress regarding binge eating
- Absence of compensatory behaviors (like purging, laxatives, or exercise)

Binge eating disorder affects eight million people in the United States and is greatly underdiagnosed. In addition, 35% of people seeking help with weight management could be clinically diagnosed with an eating disorder. Many individuals with BED are compelled to diet and often set strict restrictions for themselves which leads to overeating and feelings of guilt. The diets don't teach why this behavior is occurring in the first place, and it can take them further away from their health and weight goals. If you have concerns, we recommend that you seek help from an eating disorder specialist.

Diets have a way of becoming a security blanket, and you may fear that you will go overboard if the diet is not there to keep you in check. However, the research shows that the non-dieting approach will *not* cause your cholesterol to rise, your blood pressure to increase, or cause high blood sugar or diabetes. Removing dieting from your life will *not* cause weight gain. In fact, you are likely to see significant improvements in self-esteem and body image, as well as a reduction in disordered eating and an end to weight cycling or weight gain. We designed this workbook to help you with any food struggles you may have, while leaving diets in the past.

The Silent Victims of Dieting

What effect does this diet culture have on our children? Since half the population of adults in the United States is on a diet, there is a good chance that many families have at least one dieting parent. At a young age, children are experiencing dieting as normal and start to believe that it is a means to get healthy. What is it like for children raised in a home where their parents eat diet foods or limit their variety of foods? With the "war on obesity" constantly in the media, children are being encouraged to diet more often than ever before. Although most doctors and families have good intentions, diets can actually cause distorted relationships with food and lead to a higher prevalence of binge eating and other eating disorders in the future.

The facts are clear. Dieting behavior in children and teens is a significant predictor of weight gain and overweight. Girls who dieted frequently were 12 times more likely to binge eat compared to kids who did not diet, and boys who dieted were five times more likely to binge eat. No matter how you look at it, dieting hurts children.

REBEL Paradigm

handwritten: — = have done
handwritten: ✓ = nice

It is because of this research that we created an alternative to the dieting craze. The REBEL Against Dieting approach teaches you how to live a healthy, joyful life that is free of diets. Let's take a look at the differences:

	Dieting	REBELLING
Food	Food becomes the enemy. You find yourself constantly thinking about what you previously ate or what you will eat and find it has so much power over you. There is a lack of enjoyment as you are constantly worrying about the foods' association with your weight. You label foods as "good" or "bad" and take away permission to eat and enjoy food.	All food is equal and has a place in your daily intake. You have permission to eat what you want, when you want it and know how to put together a meal or snack that combines nutrition and enjoyment.
Snacking	Snacks are forbidden since added calories cause weight gain. You are starving at your next meal and have a hard time watching your portions. Oh well, tomorrow is a new day.	You learn to snack in between meals if you are hungry. It is OK to incorporate fun foods throughout the day, and you learn to balance them accordingly. This helps with portion control at your next meal.
Going Out to Eat	You order the same plain grilled chicken over salad, dressing on the side and salivate over someone else's more appealing lunch. Perhaps you overeat later in the day because you are not satisfied or rewarding yourself for "having a good day."	You peruse the menu and determine what you are truly hungry for. You take the time to enjoy your meal and the conversation. You stop half way through the meal, and you determine if you have eaten enough or if you need some more. If you choose to eat more, you do so without feeling guilty.
Exercise	You force yourself to work out because you "should" and are concerned with how many calories you burn during your routine. Since you exercised, it is acceptable to "treat" yourself.	You look forward to a fun exercise class you found that leaves you energized and does not seem like a chore. Your eating is not affected by exercise.
Self Esteem	You have low self-esteem during this time since all that matters is your weight. You may put your life on hold until you achieve a certain weight.	You learn to start your day with positive affirmations and appreciate what your body can do for you. The number on the scale does not indicate success.
Weight Management	You use the number on the scale to measure your success. You tend to judge your body, have unrealistic expectations, and gain a false sense of power over your weight. You ignore your body and put all your trust into the diet you are following.	You listen to your body's cues and allow your body to seek its natural weight. You accept the process, taking care of yourself throughout the journey and living a life according to your values rather than the numbers on the scale. You have higher self-esteem, a better quality of life, and begin to see your body as naturally beautiful.

If you aren't dieting, don't start. If you are dieting, keep reading with an open mind that there may be another way! It's time for you to get a *Taste of the Sweet REBELLION.*

"Everyone deserves to eat in a way that is healthful, pleasurable, and not tainted by excessive preoccupation or feelings of guilt and shame." Marci Anderson, MS, CEDRD, CPT

CHAPTER 2: Eat Like a REBEL

"Because food shouldn't make you feel bad!"™
Melissa Joy Dobbins MS, RDN, CDE, The Guilt-Free RD

Letter from Diet Prison

REBEL Dietitians,
Here are the rules I am
trying to follow:
"No eating after 6 pm"
"No restaurant foods"
"No desserts"
"No processed foods"
"No white foods"
"No carbs"
"No added sugars"
"No fried foods"
I am not sure how I can
keep this going. I am tired
and cranky.

-Dieting Darla

POST CARD
Food Police Dept.

PLACE
STAMP
HERE

Rebel Dietitians
7219 Hannover Prkway
Suite D
Greenbelt, MD
20770

Does reading Darla's food rules make you think of your own rules regarding dieting and food? Take a moment to write out the "food rules" that are keeping you trapped in the diet prison:

† no white bread, † less sugar, no finishing a pint of Haagen Das in one sitting, † no corn, no popcorn, no caffeine no fatty pork products.

† yes I intend to eat less. Have not given up my rules yet...

Next, it is important to evaluate your rules. Look over them one by one. For each rule ask yourself, *"How did I come up with this rule?"* *"Do I plan to follow this rule forever?"* In addition, the following questions can help you evaluate and reconsider your rules:

- Is this rule based on facts or fears? *facts* N A
- How does this rule inhibit relationships? How does this rule enhance them? *Others follow their own health issues as I do al*
- Do other people have to follow this rule to be okay, and if not, why do I?
- Does this rule allow for any flexibility, for unusual situations like being sick, or having an especially active week? *Hadn't thought of that ...*
- Does this rule allow for special occasions or holidays? *Yes, I honor celebrations... Lent*
- Would I tell anyone else to follow this rule? Why or why not? *No, I believe in free will*
- What am I giving up by following this rule? What am I gaining?
- What would it take to give up this rule?

(Source: *8 Keys to Recovery from an Eating Disorder* by Carolyn Costin and Gwen Schubert Grabb)

What Is Healthy?

There is so much buzz among the diet prisoners about weight and BMI, the "war on obesity," and being healthy. But, what is healthy, and what is nutritious eating?

In a world of clean, green, and extreme eating, "healthy" eating can get complicated fast. As your REBEL Dietitians®, we are here to set the record straight. Our goal for you is to live a healthy *and* happy life. This workbook outlines how you can make both of these a reality.

The good news is that you can break away from the "healthy eating" overwhelm that you find in the media, and you can redefine what healthy, happy eating is for yourself. Examples may include:

- Making dinner for your family even if it involves some convenience items.
- Going out to dinner and ordering what you are hungry for.
- Trying a new recipe and being okay with ordering pizza if what you made doesn't turn out great.

Meet REBEL Client "Marie"

MARY

Marie is a stay-at-home mom with three children, and dinner is a huge challenge. Her husband wants meat and potatoes, her kids want macaroni and cheese and chicken fingers, and Marie makes herself broiled fish over asparagus. What was once a time of bonding, relaxation, and enjoyment has now become chaotic, rushed, and exhausting as Marie attempts to make everyone happy. This process puts a strain on her time, energy, and relationships.

Marie defines "health" according to the diet she is currently on, allowing for only low carbohydrate and low calorie options. Marie struggles with eating in secret when her husband and children are in bed. When hunger sets in after under eating at dinner, she often overeats cookies and chips, feeling overly stuffed and guilty afterward.

Marie came to our office requesting a meal plan but left with so much more. We discussed her favorite meals and foods from childhood, which included meatloaf and potatoes. Marie blurted out, "This is not on my diet." "These are not healthy." "I will gain weight!" I assured her that our bodies actually need carbohydrates and explained the roles of each of the foods she had eliminated. We were able to plan these foods back into her meals and discussed balance and portions. She learned that no one food or food group can influence weight.

Eventually, Marie's children started expanding their food choices, enjoying the same foods as Mom and Dad. She felt empowered by this new information and the permission to be flexible and enjoy meals with her family. Marie was now focused on creating lasting memories around the dinner table. She was physically and emotionally satisfied, and the late night snacking slowly decreased.

Marie's years in dieting prison skewed her view of healthy eating. By practicing the REBEL skills, she learned she was able to redefine healthy, happy eating—a definition which now included flexibility and enjoyment.

Take five minutes and reflect on what healthy, happy eating means to you. Be sure to be honest with yourself. There are no right or wrong answers.

_____

_____

_____

_____

_____

_____

_____

_____

_____

_____

— like Moslems? :)

REBEL Healthy, Happy Eating Definition

As REBEL Dietitians®, we have defined healthy, happy eating to include five main pillars: Nutrition, Moderation, Balance, Variety, and Flexibility. These pillars will become the "street smarts" that you will cultivate in this workbook so that you can thrive outside of the dieting prison. Remember, these pillars are guidelines not "rules." It is important for you to decide what healthy eating looks like for yourself.

I decide ♡ :)

The Nutrition Pillar

Nutrition is the element of the REBEL process that takes the most time and thought because there is no right answer or "one-size-fits-all" meal plan. Ideally, nutrition should be a combination of enjoyment and healthier choices. We encourage you to focus on getting all of your food groups most days and balancing your individual meals versus achieving daily numeric goals. Let's break this down visually.

The REBEL Plate

Growing up, you may remember learning about the United States Department of Agriculture's (USDA) *MyPyramid* in health class. Although the guidelines were helpful, consumers found the model difficult to put into practice. In 2010, the USDA updated their materials using the *MyPlate* graphic, which helps people visualize balanced meals in everyday situations (ChooseMyPlate.gov). Here is the REBEL Dietitian® version of *MyPlate*, which includes a few extras:

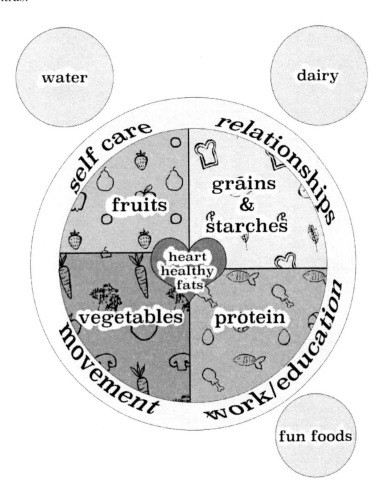

Grains and Starches

There are three macronutrients in our food that provide us with energy (calories): carbohydrates, protein, and fats. When you are in diet prison, the warden controls your meals, and you are not in charge. Often, he or she takes away a whole group of foods, frequently carbohydrates or fat. Breaking free from diet prison means you are able to eat adequate amounts of ALL these nutrients based on your individual needs.

While carbohydrates are also present in dairy, fruits, and vegetables, a typical tactic with diets is to restrict the carbohydrates from grains and starches. It is nutritionally appropriate for carbohydrates to make up 45-65% of your daily caloric needs. This will differ from person to person and may vary day to day. The daily requirement for carbohydrates is based on your height, weight, activity, and metabolic needs.

Here are some other facts about carbohydrates:

- The main function of carbohydrate metabolism is to supply the body with glucose (sugar in its simplest form) since this is the preferred source of energy for your cells. Carbohydrates are the fuel you need to do everything from walking up a flight of stairs to running a 5K!
- Even in a resting state, the brain needs a constant supply of glucose to rebuild and repair tissues and send messages to the rest of the body to power the heart, liver, kidneys, intestines, and lungs.
- Carbohydrates also help build and repair muscles. Many people think that if you want to build muscle you need to increase your protein intake; however, our body also needs glucose to drive protein into muscle cells to build lean body tissue.

Grains and starches include breads, pastas, rice, pitas, pancakes, tortillas, waffles, cereals, oatmeal, crackers, and granola. Starchy vegetables are also included in this grouping including corn, squash, and potatoes.

When choosing carbohydrates, it is important to make half of your grains "whole." This includes 100% whole grain wheat bread and pasta, brown rice, quinoa, oatmeal, and popcorn. With those guidelines, you have the luxury of choosing starches and grains (and all foods) based on nutrition as well as your options, hunger, preference, and mood. In other words, you can have white pasta for dinner, then you can use whole wheat bread for your lunchtime sandwiches. Whole grain or not, the portions are still the same. Being a REBEL means that you can pick and choose what works for you.

In our experience, the starch and grains quadrant of the REBEL Plate is usually where most people report they are overeating, and they often express concern about the amounts they should consume. It is very easy to have three servings of cereal or pasta at each meal. This is part of the reason why when people eliminate carbohydrates, they may initially experience some weight loss. However, it wasn't the food that caused the weight gain; it was most likely the portions! We recommend that grains and starches take up about one quarter of your plate to start (or about the size of your fist), choosing whichever grains or starches you prefer while sticking to the initial portions, savoring each bite, and reassessing your hunger to determine if you need more. (We will discuss this process in Chapter 3.)

What are your favorite grains and starches? What are your favorite whole grain options?

_____

_____

_____

Are there any grains or starches that you overeat or avoid? What portion do you typically have? Does this feel like too much, too little, or just right? How can you adjust these portions to feel more comfortable around these foods?

_____

_____

_____

Proteins

Protein typically makes up about 10-25% of the calories in your diet, a percentage that should be customized for the individual. Essential functions of this nutrient include:

- Building and repairing muscle, skin, and other body tissues
- Maintaining organ systems
- Producing hormones
- Fortifying the immune system to fight infections
- Balancing blood sugar levels
- Helping us feel more satisfied after meals

Most Americans already get enough protein. Unfortunately, what we find is while breakfast and snacks often provide little to no protein, lunch and dinner follow with larger portions of protein which can throw off a person's hunger cues. On the other hand, when we balance protein throughout the day, it helps us to feel satisfied. Keep in mind that you do not need to have meat from animals, poultry, or fish at each meal to be sure you are getting enough protein. You can also find protein in dairy products, beans, quinoa, nuts, seeds, and vegetables. There is also some protein in whole grains such as oatmeal, whole wheat bread, and brown rice.

Consuming some protein at each meal and snack can help you feel full and help keep blood sugars stable. A breakfast of cereal and fruit (limited protein) is going to leave you hungry in an hour or so and craving foods later in the day. In addition, these low protein meals may cause your energy levels to suffer, and your mood may be irritable from being hungry—not that you would be to blame if you became tired and hungry! The best thing to do is not to let that happen. Embrace protein at each meal and snack!

What are your favorite sources of protein?

_____

_____

_____

How can you incorporate protein in your meals?

Breakfast: _____

Lunch: _____

Dinner: _____

Snacks: _____

Fruits and Vegetables

As you can see, fruits and vegetables take up half the REBEL Plate. In general, aim for an average of five servings of fruits and vegetables a day. Since a serving is either ½ cup cooked or one cup of raw fruits or vegetables, you might not need to include these with every meal and snack to reach this goal. For example, a salad with a lettuce base and additional vegetable toppings may easily include three to four servings!

Produce of similar colors represent a unique nutrient profile of vitamins and minerals, so variety is key. There really is science behind "eat the colors of the rainbow." Fruits and vegetables are the main source of antioxidants, helping to repair cell damage and reduce a person's risk of cancer, cardiac disease, cataracts, and diabetes. The macronutrient present in fruit is carbohydrates. Vegetables contain some carbohydrates (less than fruit) and protein. You can see the complete list of micronutrients, or vitamins and minerals found in produce, in the REBEL Toolbox.

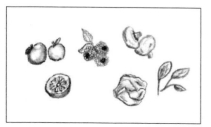

Although supplements can provide individual nutrients, they are better absorbed through food. For example, by eating one carrot you are ingesting hundreds of nutrients, phytochemicals, and antioxidants, and these work together to protect us from disease. You would need to take multiple supplements to mimic the nutrient variety contained in just one vegetable or fruit. Just as we encourage you not to label foods as "bad" we also caution you about labeling foods as "good," which may set you up to overeat them. Although most of us would label fruits and vegetables as "good," the goal is not to eat any foods in excess just because of their "healthy" labels.

When looking at the REBEL Plate, we often find that the starches/grains and protein quadrants are easily filled; however, many people struggle to fit fruits and vegetables into their meals. Possible causes include:

- Parents not allowing dessert until their children have finished their vegetables.
- Fruits and vegetables spoiling more quickly than other convenience foods, which can mean more waste and frequent grocery shopping.
- Shoppers may be confused on how to choose ripe produce, or they may be unsure how to prepare it.
- Some people may have an enhanced sense of taste causing them to hesitate when trying some vegetables and fruits.
- People eat out more frequently today and may not have access to many choices when it comes to fruits or vegetables.
- Preparing produce can require more effort such as washing, peeling, and cutting.
- Fruits and vegetables are typically associated with diet foods, which are "mandated" on diet programs, so naturally there may be an aversion to them.

Whatever the reason, it seems that produce is often missing in our diets. How can we make this half of the plate as tasty and convenient as the grains and protein half? Remember, fruits and vegetables taste best when they are fresh and in season. Strawberries that have to be transported long distances from the farm to the store in the winter taste (and cost) much different from strawberries grown locally in the summer. If possible, purchase fruits and vegetables at a farmers' market or farm stand. Produce sold in season and grown near the point of sale not only tastes better and has better nutrition quality, your purchases also support local farmers.

REBEL Tip: Look for Community Supported Agriculture (CSA) programs in your area, which allow you to get local produce delivered to your door.

For convenience, you can also use frozen or canned produce. Frozen produce is easy to keep on hand and allows you to buy your favorite fruits and vegetables even when they are not in season. Frozen and canned produce may also be more economical than fresh. Items are picked and frozen at the peak of freshness, locking in the nutrients. In some cases, they may actually contain more nutrients than fresh depending on how far the fresh produce has traveled before reaching your table. Although frozen produce is typically not preserved with sugar or salt, be sure to check the ingredient labels to see if anything extra was added.

Canned fruits and vegetables are also picked at peak ripeness, and the canning process helps lock in key nutrients. For canned fruit, aim for options packed in its own juice or 100% fruit juice. When it comes to canned vegetables, sodium is often added as a flavor enhancer and preservative.

REBEL Tip: Rinse canned vegetables in a colander to remove about 40% of the sodium! Canned produce is another budget saver!

A question clients often ask is, *"What about juicing or smoothies?"* Sometimes it can be easier to consume fruits and vegetables in liquid form; however, you want to make sure you are getting as many whole fruits and vegetables as possible to ensure high fiber intake. When you juice, you may get the vitamins and minerals, but the high fiber pulp is removed and thrown away. On the other hand, when creating your favorite smoothie, the whole fruit or vegetable goes into the blender which will include the fiber.

Here are some REBELLIOUS ways to enjoy fruits and vegetables:

1. Add spinach to your next smoothie!
2. Cook with fruit to add some sweetness to your meal. For example, we love how apples compliment pork chops.
3. Rather than use a jar of sauce, top your next bowl of pasta or pizza with fresh, diced tomatoes.
4. Add some ripe berries to a summer salad for a sweet burst of flavor.
5. Add red or orange peppers to your sandwich for color and crunch.
6. Throw peaches on the grill on a summer day along with the steaks for a fun side dish.
7. Make an omelet or quiche full of mushrooms and broccoli.
8. Add mangos, pineapples, or apricots in fresh salsa to use as a side dish or to top grilled chicken or fish.
9. Add a serving of vegetables into your starch side at dinner. Mix some spinach or other leafy greens into your rice or mash cooked carrots into your potatoes.
10. Use fruit such as strawberries and bananas for dessert. Dip in Nutella® or serve over ice cream.
11. Sweeten plain oatmeal or create your own parfait by layering yogurt with fresh fruit.
12. Try "eggplant fries" or "carrot fries" drizzled with oil, sprinkled with salt, seasoned with spices, and roasted in the oven.
13. Mix blueberries or bananas into homemade waffles or pancakes.
14. Try a new recipe such as carrot soufflé or spinach balls.

List all your favorite fruits and vegetables:

_____

_____

Are there any fruits and vegetables you would like to try?

_____

_____

How can you incorporate more fruits and/or vegetables in your meals?

Breakfast: _____

Lunch: _____

Dinner: _____

Snacks: _____

Dairy

Milk products often get the ax in many diet plans, yet dairy is one of the most nutrient dense groups on the plate! Please do not give up on milk, yogurt, cheese, and ice cream if you don't have to—meaning you have not been diagnosed with lactose intolerance or a dairy allergy.

The main nutrients we derive from this food group include carbohydrates, protein, calcium (in a form readily absorbed by the body), vitamin D, phosphorus, magnesium, and potassium. While there are other ways to get calcium in your diet, dairy foods rank among the highest sources.

In adults, a calcium deficiency, along with other factors, may result in bone deterioration called osteoporosis. We recommend aiming for three servings of dairy on most days. A serving of dairy is probably smaller than you think: eight ounces of milk (or milk substitute), one ounce of cheese, or six ounces of yogurt.

With yogurt in particular, be mindful of added sweeteners and other artificial ingredients. You may also consider trying plain yogurt and adding your own fruit, sugar, syrup, vanilla, or cinnamon.

How can you incorporate dairy in your meals? Note: snacks are a great place to make sure you get in all your three servings!

Breakfast: _____

Lunch: _____

Dinner: _____

Snacks: _____

Heart Healthy Fats

Dietary fat occurs naturally in nuts, seeds, whole grains, dairy, and meats. It is also added to food during preparation such as when you sauté or bake. Since many people limit fat intake as a means to lose weight, we wanted to highlight its importance as part of a well-rounded plate.

Dietary fat typically accounts for 30–35% of our daily calorie needs. Fat in our food DOES NOT equal fat on our bodies. Yes, heart healthy fats are higher in calories per serving when compared to carbohydrates and proteins, but the key is being aware of the portion size, determining what you are hungry for, and letting fat do its job to add taste and satiety to your meals. Embracing fat and not fighting it may actually help you ward off excessive intake of food later in the day and may even raise the good cholesterol that your body needs. Heart healthy fat sources include olive oil, canola oil, nut butters, nuts, avocados, flax seeds, and chia seeds. Dietary fats serve us by enhancing the taste of foods, providing satiety, and absorbing fat-soluble vitamins (A, D, E, and K). Fat is essential for brain and hormone development. Fat also maintains healthy hair, skin, and nails!

"Fat makes you beautiful!" Carlene Thomas, RD
The Wedding Wellness Workbook: Your Nutrition How-To Before "I Do"

What heart healthy fats do you already use?

_____

How can you incorporate heart healthy fat in your meals?

Breakfast: _____

Lunch: _____

Dinner: _____

Snacks: _____

Fun Foods

Many times in our work, we see what diets have done to our clients' relationships with once loved and admired foods. These foods become the enemy even though they may indeed be a favorite. Do you remember when you were a child and you weren't thinking about calories and weight—you were just loving and enjoying food? Can you remember what your favorite food was at age five or ten? We have been asking our clients these questions and love the answers we are receiving, *"Mom's homemade Christmas cookies," "Drumsticks® from the ice cream truck,"* and a forgotten favorite, *"DunkAroos™!"* It is so nice to see clients forget about their body concerns, counting calories, and losing weight while they remember a time when food was fun and enjoyable.

Here are some tips for enjoying fun foods. Every time you are going to eat something, first decide what you are in the mood for, and then figure out how you can incorporate that food into a balanced meal or snack. For example, a snack of two cookies and a bowl of fruit (both with the main macronutrient carbohydrates) may not do much for your satiety. Yet, pairing this with a glass of milk or cottage cheese adds protein, which can make this snack both fun and satisfying!

"Having a healthy relationship with the foods you love and truly enjoying them is key to a healthy lifestyle." Alex Raymond, REBEL Intern

What was your favorite food as a child?

_____

What was your favorite food as a teenager?

_____

How do you think you can incorporate your favorite fun foods into your meals and snacks?

_____

_____

Water

We wanted to add water to the REBEL Plate as a reminder to stay hydrated throughout the day. The symptoms of dehydration such as fatigue, irritability, and headaches can often be confused for hunger, leading us to eat more. Water is also important for keeping bowel movements regular and preventing constipation. Water is cheap and an easy addition to your beauty regimen as it helps hydrate skin. Did you know that water intake can also affect emotions, energy, and mental performance?

Tired of Drinking Plain Water?

Try some of these fun, flavorful recipes!

Faux Soda
- 1 c. club soda or seltzer water
- ¼ c. orange or cranberry juice

Cucumber Water
- 6 c. of water
- 12 thin slices of cucumber
- Mint (optional)

Mint and Lemon
- 1 quart of water
- 2 lemons, cut in slices
- 3–4 large mint sprigs

Strawberry and Cantaloupe
- 1 quart of water
- 4 long wedges of cantaloupe, cut into small pieces
- 12 strawberries, cut in half

Cherry Limeade
- 1 quart water, still or sparkling
- 1 key lime, sliced thinly
- 6 pitted cherries
- 1 sprig of mint

We view nutrition as nourishing your mind, body, and spirit, which includes other areas of your life. We have included these on the plate since they influence **what**, **where**, **when**, **why**, and **how** you eat.

Movement

Although we devote a whole section later in this workbook to movement, we wanted to point to its place on the REBEL Plate as a reminder of how important movement is to our well-being and health. Movement is a way for us to stay connected with our bodies, provide energy, and boost mood. In addition, movement can help conquer stress and emotional eating. Your nutritional needs will depend on what movement you enjoy, the time spent, and intensity of your activity. Just as with food, we encourage our clients to think back to what they enjoyed doing as a child to reconnect to movement in a positive way.

Self-Care

This topic is also discussed more in depth later in the workbook, but we wanted to remind you that stress, illness, and lack of sleep can also affect your eating. It is important to keep this area of your life in balance so that your nutrition can do its job. Self-care plays a key role in the REBEL approach.

Work/Education

Work and school often take priority during the day, and we put our health and nutrition on the backburner. Priorities aside, working in an office or being at school can also affect when you can (or cannot) eat. It is important to evaluate how this affects your eating habits so you can make a plan that fits healthy, happy eating into your busy lifestyle.

Relationships

Eating with others may help slow down your eating if you are actively listening or conversing with others. Try having a lunch date in the cafe or kitchenette with a co-worker or eating breakfast with a family member. Even when not eating with others, it is important to take care of yourself and prioritize your meals. Try eating at the table at home or leaving your office at work to take your lunch outside or to a common area to help you focus on and enjoy your meal.

 Is there anything else you would add to your REBEL Plate?

_____

_____

The Moderation Pillar

The second pillar of healthy, happy eating is moderation. Just as any one thing—from asparagus to ice cream to water—is not healthful in excess, everything can be healthful in moderation. This can be difficult for lifetime dieters to grasp since they have been placing "good" and "bad" labels on food for many years. Moderation comes from the inside out since our bodies can help us dictate what we are hungry for and how much we need. More on this in chapter 3. **Remember, it's not just what you are eating or the calories, but how much, why, and how often that make a difference.**

We encourage you to use your hand to help you determine portion sizes. This gives you a starting point, then you can check in with your hunger and fullness to determine if you need more (or perhaps less the next time). Your hand will be there on vacation, out to eat, and at Grandma's house; therefore, you do not need to rely on measuring cups, food scales, or special containers:

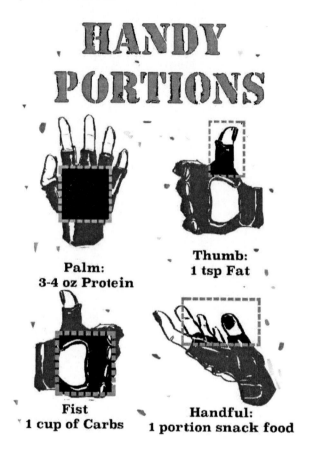

HANDY PORTIONS

Palm:
3-4 oz Protein

Thumb:
1 tsp Fat

Fist
1 cup of Carbs

Handful:
1 portion snack food

How does a REBEL think about portions? Remember portion sizes are general guidelines for the whole population and a good place to start when plating your meals and snacks. After you have had time to enjoy and digest your meal, you can check in with your hunger to determine if you may need a greater or smaller portion the next time.

For example, if you are in the mood for pancakes (grains with main macronutrient carbohydrates) at breakfast, start with one serving and pair with eggs (main macronutrient protein) and walnuts (main macronutrient fat). Just having pancakes and home fries for a meal may leave you hungry soon afterwards since they both have the main macronutrient carbohydrates. Choose the starch that is most enjoyable to you in that moment and balance the rest of the plate accordingly.

The Balance Pillar

As we start with many of our clients, our REBEL Plate is a great tool for understanding balance. Different foods work together to give your body the right amount of nutrients. For example, starting your day with a meal that only includes foods from the same food group will leave you fatigued, hungry, or wanting more. Strive to balance your meals to include all three macronutrients—carbohydrates, protein, and fat—to help keep you appropriately full, your blood sugars stable, and your energy levels up. Snacks might only include two macronutrients. For example, a balanced snack could include peanut butter (a fat) and crackers (a carbohydrate).

The Variety Pillar

Variety is the spice of a REBELLIOUS life. Even the most balanced meals eaten in moderation may not provide optimal nutrition. For example, if you eat a picture perfect plate of chicken, broccoli, and brown rice every day, you will still not get the full complement of nutrients you need. As mentioned before, each color represents a different nutrient profile, so eating a variety of foods will maximize the amount of nutrients in your diet. Eating a wide range of foods also appeals to all of your senses, satisfying unique textures, tastes, and smells to make mealtime adventurous!

Eating a wide variety of foods also allows you to practice portions and balance, so you can mix it up each day and not feel obligated to eat all of your favorite foods in one sitting. Alternating between two starches, i.e. pancakes and home fries at breakfast, allows you to enjoy two foods you love while still paying attention to your portions of carbohydrates as well as allowing room for food from other groups!

The Flexibility Pillar

Since the examples above won't happen every time you are eating, flexibility helps you put the fun back in food. Without flexibility in your diet, preparing and eating meals can become exhausting. Being flexible helps you to plan your next meal and keeps food in its place, not allowing it to take over your life. Here is our favorite definition of "normal eating" by Ellyn Satter who teaches her clients to embrace the importance of flexibility:

"Normal eating is going to the table hungry and eating until you are satisfied. It is being able to **choose food you like** and eat it and truly get enough of it—not just stop eating because you think you should. Normal eating is being able to give some thought to your food selection so you get nutritious food, but not being so wary and restrictive that you miss out on enjoyable food. Normal eating is giving yourself permission to eat sometimes because you are happy, sad, or bored, or just because it feels good. Normal eating is mostly three meals a day, or four or five, or it can be choosing to munch along the way. It is leaving some cookies on the plate because you know you can have some again tomorrow, or it is eating more now because they taste so wonderful. Normal eating is overeating at times, feeling stuffed and uncomfortable. And it can be under-eating at times and wishing you had more. Normal eating is **trusting your body** to make up for your mistakes in eating. Normal eating takes up some of your time and attention, but keeps its place as only one important area of your life. In short, normal eating is *flexible*. It varies in response to your hunger, your schedule, your proximity to food and your feelings." ~ Ellyn Satter, MS, RDN, MSSW *Secrets of Feeding a Healthy Family: How to Eat, How to Raise Good Eaters, How to Cook*

Now, how wonderful is that? What we love is that food was never intended to be PERFECT. Normal eating gives you the freedom to be flexible, to make mistakes in eating, and to know that your body can make up for it. Trust is a huge part in this definition. Soon you will be able to trust yourself around foods you may have overeaten in the past, trust yourself at a buffet, trust yourself at Christmas dinner, and trust yourself at the grocery store. When you experience TRUST and tranquility around food that is a good sign that your relationship with food has been mended and strengthened.

REBELIZE Your Meal Planning

In order to fit these five pillars (Nutrition, Moderation, Balance, Variety, and Flexibility) into a busy lifestyle, being prepared is key. Meal planning allows us to take our nutrition knowledge and apply it to our daily lives. For some it may mean picking out two new recipes to try, and for others it may mean planning meals for each day. Everyone is different and you have to find what works for you.

Meal planning is not about setting strict rules or having boring meals day after day. In fact, meal planning can help you prepare meals that you will look forward to as opposed to plain "diet approved" food that is repetitive and mundane. Here are some meal planning tips:

1. **First, map out your week.** Identify the nights you will be working late, what appointments you have, and the nights your kids have activities. You won't want to plan a dinner that requires extensive preparation on these nights! Maybe you will have leftovers on those occasions. Be realistic, and plan which nights you will eat out and list your dining options. Use a scheduling system familiar to you such as Google Calendars, Outlook, or even a large white board or scratch pad in your office or kitchen.

2. **Try scheduling themes for the days of the week** to narrow down your options and help with grocery shopping. You can list by cuisine or the cooking method for the meal. Your themes might look like:

> ### Meal Themes for Next Week:
> ☐ Monday—Meatless
> ☐ Tuesday—Italian
> ☐ Wednesday—Mexican
> ☐ Thursday—Leftovers
> ☐ Friday—Soup and Salad
> ☐ Saturday—Slow Cooker
> ☐ Sunday—Stir-Fry

3. **Attempt for a balance** of carbohydrates, fat, and protein in your meals.

4. **Keep your freezer organized** by labeling and dating whatever meals or food items you have in stock. Use what you have to help plan your meals for the week.

5. **Sketch out some backup meals** and keep the necessary ingredients on hand for when your plans are shaken up (and you know that will happen!)

Items to Keep in Your Pantry

- Canned black beans and chickpeas
- Tuna packets that do not require draining
- Uncle Ben's® 90 Second Brown Rice
- White and sweet potatoes
- Whole grain bread, pitas, and tortillas for a quick sandwich or wrap
- Cans or cartons of low sodium soup
- Various forms of pasta and dried noodles
- Slivered almonds, sunflower seeds, or dried fruits
- Peanut butter or other nut butters
- Canned fruits and vegetables

Items to Keep in Your Refrigerator

- Vegetables such as sliced cucumbers, baby carrots, and cherry tomatoes (prepare at the beginning of the week or purchase a party tray. Store in storage bags)
- Cheeses like Fontina, Gorgonzola, or shredded cheddar
- Cold cuts
- Pre-washed salad greens, spinach, and salad dressing
- Condiments like salsa, mustard, and soy sauce to kick up entrées
- Greek yogurt and cottage cheese
- Eggs (for a quick protein option)

Items to Keep in Your Freezer

- Frozen vegetables like broccoli, cauliflower, carrots, green beans, spinach, or mixed vegetables
- Frozen fruit such as berries, pineapples, or cherries. You can even peel aging bananas and throw in the freezer for smoothies later!
- Frozen meat and fish items that can be used with vegetables or pantry staples: ground meat and burgers (beef, turkey, and/or veggie), meatballs, shrimp, fish fillets, chicken pieces or boneless breasts
- Frozen entrées (which we consider "emergency meals") for a quick meal in a pinch
- Frozen waffles for breakfast, lunch, or dinner

Grocery Shopping

Here are five **REBEL Tips** to make grocery shopping more enjoyable and efficient:

1. **Keep a running grocery list** on your phone so you always have it with you in case you run to the store after work! You can keep track of all the staple items you buy weekly and move them to the top as you run out. It is also easy to add to the list when you come across a new recipe.

2. **Consider using a grocery delivery company.** These popular services can be helpful for those weeks when you cannot get to the store. You can shop online and have it delivered to your door! While there is a delivery fee, you may actually save money by not going out to eat or ordering takeout when the refrigerator is bare. You also will not be tempted to pick up things not on your list. Check to see if your local store has this service.

3. **Don't be afraid to shop in the middle of the store.** Just because the fresh foods are in the perimeter, it does not mean the rest of the store is off-limits. If a family member has a birthday coming up, you may find yourself in the baking aisle to create something special. Whole grains, beans, canned vegetables and fruits, spices, and sauces are all found in the center aisles. REBEL and explore!

4. **Think of grocery shopping as an investment.** Don't be afraid to buy things that are prepared, chopped, and washed if that means you will use them and they will make your cooking experience less stressful. While these prepared items tend to be more expensive, you may be saving money in the long run if you are able to eat at home more often. You may also save money because these prepared foods will get used up, whereas the whole foods may go bad before you get to them.

5. **Bring some positivity to the grocery shopping experience** and try making it something you actually enjoy. If you dread going to the grocery store, consider listening to your favorite music, sip a hot beverage, or shop with a friend. If possible, avoid peak hours when lines are long and aisles are crowded.

Sample Grocery List

Colorful Vegetables:	**Colorful Fruits:**
Fresh:	*Fresh*:
Eggplant	Apples
Spinach	Bananas
Onions	Pineapple
Fresh garlic	Grapes
Sweet potatoes and white potatoes	
Red bell pepper	*Frozen/canned:*
Green bell pepper	Frozen strawberries
Yellow bell pepper	Frozen blueberries
Cucumbers	Canned peaches
Baby carrots	Toasted coconut flakes
Frozen/canned:	
Canned tomatoes	
Corn	
Stir-fry vegetable mix	
Tomato sauce	
Lean Protein:	**Breads/Grains (Whole grain bread/pasta/rice):**
Ground beef	White bread
Silken tofu	Corn tortillas
Canned tuna	Spaghetti
Chicken breasts	Rice
Hummus	Popcorn
Eggs	Pretzels
Cashews	Pita chips
Dairy (yogurt, milk, cheese):	**Beverages:**
Vanilla Greek yogurt	Cranberry juice
Milk	Seltzer water
Parmesan cheese, grated	Red Wine
Mexican blend cheese, shredded	
Fun Foods:	**Containers/Packaging:**
Red velvet cupcake mix	Aluminum foil
Cream cheese frosting	Glass containers
Ben and Jerry's® New York Super Fudge Chunk Ice Cream	Cling wrap
	Cupcake tins

Now create your own grocery list for the week:

Grocery List	
Colorful Vegetables: *Fresh:* *Frozen/canned:*	**Colorful Fruits:** *Fresh:* *Frozen/canned:*
Lean Protein:	**Breads/Grains:**
Dairy (yogurt, milk, cheese):	**Beverages:**
Fun Foods:	**Containers/Packaging:**

Reading the Food Label

One of the reasons that grocery shopping may cause some anxiety is the sea of labels staring back at you. While the nutrition facts label is a wonderful tool that allows you to take ownership over your food choices, the label often has a lot of numbers, categories, and various measurements that can be confusing. Specifically, if you are trying to get in and out of the grocery store, dissecting the entire label can be time-consuming. Here are the things that we do and don't look at on a nutrition facts label, some of which you may find surprising:

Ingredients: Whole Grain Oats (includes oat bran), Sugar, Modified Corn Starch, Honey, Brown Sugar Syrup, Salt, Tripotassium Phosphate, Canola Oil, Natural Almond Flavor, Vitamin E Added to preserve Freshness.

Vitamins and Minerals: Calcium Carbonate, Zinc and Iron, Vitamin C, Niacin, Vitamin B6, Vitamin B2, Vitamin B1, Vitamin A, Vitamin B12, Folic Acid, Vitamin D3.

May Contain: Wheat, Nuts, Soy Products

We DO Look at the Serving Size

This is important to consider when you determine how much of a food you're actually consuming. For example when it comes to cereal many people eat between three to four cups whereas the serving size calls for ½ to ¾ of a cup. This is helpful to use as a guide when planning your meals. Determine what may be tasty and satisfying and what other food items could help round out the meal.

REBEL Tip: Top Greek yogurt with cereal and nuts to help make this meal more satisfying.

We DON'T Look at Calories

Remember, lower calories does not equal better calories. Calories are not always the best indicator of the quality of the food! Do you want to eat a low calorie food just to be hungry an hour later? No deal!

We DON'T Look at the Grams of Fat

We are not too concerned with how much fat is in something. Rather, we are concerned with the type of fat it is. For example, nuts and peanut butter have a high amount of fat, but it is unsaturated fat which helps to lower triglycerides, cholesterol, and inflammation in the body all while helping to increase good (HDL) cholesterol.

We DO Look at the Grams of Saturated and Trans Fat

These are the types of fats to keep to a minimum. Trans fats contribute to elevated cholesterol, and the goal is to look for food options with 0 grams trans fat.

We DON'T Look at the Percent Daily Value

The percent daily value is the percentage of macro- or micro-nutrients that you need each day based on a 2000 calorie diet. This can be confusing since individuals often need more or less calories depending on age, gender, height, weight, and activity level.

We DO Look at the Ingredients

After the Nutrition Facts label, the ingredients list is one of the most important things to read. Look for food items with whole ingredients, and pay attention to how many total ingredients are in a food item. We recommend natural peanut butter or real ice cream over a product with artificial sweeteners and other preservatives.

Keep in mind that depending on your specific nutrition and health goals, you may need to pay more attention to certain nutrition facts. Of course, every part of the nutrition label on each individual food item is not going to show perfect nutrition every time—another reminder of why variety is important! Overall, the key is to try to choose whole foods that are satisfying and that you enjoy. It is also important to allow flexibility in your diet and choose a nice balance of healthy and great-tasting foods.

Cooking at Home

We are big advocates of cooking at home which allows you to use more whole ingredients and be in charge of the balance and portions of the meal. Of course, this is not always practical and you can certainly be a REBEL outside of the house, but cooking dinner at home a few nights a week can make a huge impact on your health. Make sure your kitchen is clean and organized, and throw out expired condiments, spices, and freezer food. Play music and light candles. Your kitchen should be a relaxing, spa-like environment that feels safe and welcoming.

"Cook with kindness. Don't let perfectionism stand in the way of getting your hands dirty." Klara Knezevic, REBEL Intern

REBEL Kitchen Essentials

1. **Salad spinner:** If you are purchasing whole heads of lettuce you must have a salad spinner. Try washing and bagging your lettuce right after bringing it home from the grocery store. This way your salad greens are ready to go and you avoid throwing away wilted lettuce at the end of the week.

   REBEL Tip: Store cut lettuce in storage bags or containers with paper towels to keep it fresh for up to two weeks! Salads and sandwich toppings are now much easier.

2. **Storage containers:** We recommend glass storage containers for meal planning and cooking ahead. In particular, glass containers are easy to clean and are both freezer and microwave safe.

3. **Chef's knife:** You may have a whole knife set, but we recommend investing in a good knife that gets used over and over. Keep your knife sharp to make slicing easy and safe.

4. **Blender or food processor:** You know they are great for making smoothies, but they are also great time savers when it comes to chopping vegetables, making homemade dips such as hummus and guacamole, or whipping up homemade dressings using your own ingredients.

5. **Meat thermometer:** This helps you cook your meats safely without overcooking them and ending up with a dry chicken breast or charred steak.

6. **Sauté pan or wok:** One of the quickest forms of cooking is stir-frying. It is an easy way to combine proteins, grains, and vegetables all in one dish! Using a wok or deep sauté pan makes mixing easier.

7. **Sheet pan (cookie sheet):** Sheet pans can be used for just about everything from baking, to roasting vegetables, and warming up leftovers in the oven.

8. **Mason jars:** These double for storage containers and can add some decor to your kitchen. Store spices, grains, or coffee. Date and label the bottom and arrange on open shelves. You can also use mason jars to store salads and vegetables in your fridge!

9. **George Foreman® grill:** George Foreman grills are great for quick grilling inside during the winter or in a dorm or apartment. You can make burgers, sausages, chicken, or vegetables. You can even make paninis with them!

10. **Table decor:** Festive and colorful plates, unscented candles, beautiful serving dishes, and placemats are some examples of ways to dress up your meals, making them more enjoyable whether they are with family and friends or you are dining alone.

Take time to set the table with unique table decor at your next meal.
Take a picture and share with the REBEL Dietitians® using #REBELDiets!

List what you may need to make cooking easier and exciting:

_____

_____

_____

_____

_____

_____

REBEL Meal Ideas

Based on the information we provided, here are some of our favorite ideas for REBELLIOUS meals and snacks. Aim for three food groups (or more) in each meal to make sure you have a good balance of nutrients. Shoot for at least two food groups in snacks. Remember, this is meal planning, not perfection. Cooking at home does not have to be elaborate. See the REBEL Toolbox for recipes!

Breakfast

Eggs are such a versatile food! Make them scrambled, poached, over easy, hard boiled; the list goes on. Are you running late for work? Try making scrambled eggs in a mug and pair with an English muffin or toast! This can be done at home or at work! You can also make eggs in a muffin tin ahead of time and freeze them. Microwave them briefly in the morning when you are running short on time. Other egg ideas include:

- Adding some chopped vegetables to an omelet or scramble. Try bell peppers, spinach, onions, mushrooms, or tomatoes.
- Serving quiche with a side of garlicky, sautéed kale.
- Making some huevos rancheros for eggs with a spicy kick in the morning.

Breakfast toasts are a great way to start your morning. Sure, you can top your toast with peanut butter and jelly, but don't be afraid to get creative! Choose one ingredient from each group (bread, spread, and topping) to create a balanced, high-energy meal! Try meat, cheeses, avocado, or hummus. Find more options in the REBEL Toolbox:

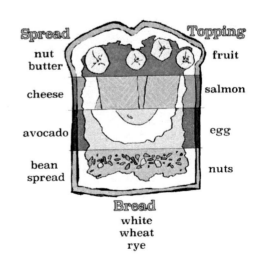

Spread: nut butter, cheese, avocado, bean spread

Topping: fruit, salmon, egg, nuts

Bread: white, wheat, rye

- Salmon and Cream Cheese Breakfast Toast
- Avocado and Cheese Breakfast Toast
- Peanut Butter and Banana Breakfast Toast
- Refried Beans and Cheese Breakfast Toast

Yogurt parfaits are simple to make in the morning or even the night before. All you need are three ingredients—yogurt, fruit, and some granola (or other crunchy topping). Try topping high protein Greek yogurt with fresh or frozen fruit. Top with your choice of chia seeds, flax seeds, slivered almonds, granola, or dried cereal. See the REBEL Toolbox for more REBEL parfait recipes.

Old fashioned oatmeal can be the base for a delicious and satisfying breakfast. Our REBEL Toolbox provides you with step-by-step recipes to make oatmeal different and fun.

For example, try mixing a spoonful of peanut butter and cocoa powder for a peanut butter cup inspired cereal. Or add a scoop of pureed pumpkin, cinnamon, nutmeg, and cloves for a warm bowl of pumpkin spice oatmeal. Craving breakfast with a tropical flare? Add bananas, pineapple juice, and coconut flakes!

.5 cup Oats
1 cup Milk

Microwave 2.5 - 3 minutes on high

Smoothies make a great blend-and-go breakfast! You can easily mix and match a variety of fruits, vegetables, proteins, and liquids, even adding ingredients like oats, nuts, and seeds! For easier blending, layer your ingredients in the pitcher starting with the liquid, then add your protein, fruit and/or vegetables, and other crunchy ingredients. Flavor with sweeteners if needed (agave syrup, honey, or maple syrup) or spices (nutmeg, cinnamon, pumpkin pie spice, mint, or basil). Don't be afraid to experiment. Our favorite combinations for smoothies, like the Cheesecake Smoothie, the Chocolate Peanut Butter Smoothie, and the Blueberry Banana Smoothie, are in the REBEL Toolbox.

SMOOTHIE

1. fruit–fresh or frozen

bananas blueberries peaches blackberries raspberries strawberries mangoes

2. protein

Greek yogurt silken tofu hemp hearts protein powder cotttage cheese

3. liquid

water coconut water 100% fruit juice milk coconut milk soy milk rice milk almond milk

4. add-ins

peanut butter oats cocoa powder chia seeds almonds flax seeds

Plan your breakfasts for one week. Include ingredients you need or the restaurant to go to if eating away from home. It is okay to duplicate, but aim for some variety!

	Menu Items	Groceries Needed or Restaurant
Monday		
Tuesday		
Wednesday		
Thursday		
Friday		
Saturday		
Sunday		

Lunches

Lunch can be a difficult meal for many of us if our busy schedules keep us from pausing to eat! Check out the REBEL ideas below. Recipes from the REBEL Toolbox are in **bold**.

Main Entrees	Protein Power
Pinwheel Wraps	**Hard Boiled Eggs**
• **Peanut Butter and Jelly**	**Hummus**
• **Cream Cheese and Cucumber**	**Homemade Energy Bites**
• **Turkey and Cheese**	**Roasted Chickpeas**
• **Hummus and Vegetables**	Turkey pepperoni
Cold Vegetable Pizza	Sunflower seeds
Black Bean and Turkey Chili	Grilled chicken cubes
Pasta Salad with Vegetables and Chickpeas	Protein bars (10 grams or more protein per serving)
Avocado Tuna Salad	Cottage cheese
Honey Mustard Tuna Salad	Cheese stick
Egg Salad Sandwich	Yogurt (try freezing them to keep your lunch cold!
Taco Salad	
Beans and Rice	
Grilled Chicken Quesadilla	
Rotisserie Chicken Honey Raisin Chicken Salad	
Rotisserie Chicken Basic Chicken Salad	
Quinoa Surprise	
Fruits and Vegetables	Fun Foods
Baked Apples or Pears with Cinnamon	**Trail Mix**
Bananas and Peanut Butter Whip	**Kale Chips**
Natural apple sauce	Pudding cups
Yogurt covered blueberries	Chocolate covered raisins
Fruit salad	Popcorn
Cucumber and tomato Salad	Whole grain fig bar cookies
Carrot fries	Whole wheat pretzels
Fruit kebobs	Whole grain muffins
Raw carrots, green peppers, broccoli, celery, snap peas, cucumber slices, cauliflower, etc…	Graham crackers

Take a stab at planning your lunches for one week. Include ingredients you need or restaurant if eating away from home:

	Menu Items	Groceries Needed or Restaurant
Monday		
Tuesday		
Wednesday		
Thursday		
Friday		
Saturday		
Sunday		

Dinner

Dinner does not have to be a lavish, gourmet meal like you might see on a television cooking show. You can make easy dinners at home that are tasty, nutritious, and won't leave you stressed at the end of the day. Try some of the ideas below. You will find more detailed recipes in the REBEL Toolbox.

Potato-based entrées can be prepared quickly using a microwave. Prepare a baked potato or sweet potato by rinsing and scrubbing clean, then puncture the skin several times with a knife or fork. Microwave for five minutes. Let rest for a few minutes. Top with a protein source, cheeses, and/or vegetables. Some great options to try include:

- Baked potato or sweet potato with chili
- Baked potato or sweet potato with cheese and broccoli
- Baked potato or sweet potato with grilled chicken

Sandwiches are not just for lunch! Sandwiches are portable meals you can eat when running from place to place that also provide nutrition from two or three food groups. Pair sandwiches with soups, chili, salads, or a bowl of fresh fruit to round out your meal. Here are some ideas to try:

- Grilled cheese and soup
- Pesto chicken panini
- BBQ chicken quesadilla
- Tuna melt

Stir-fries can be a great way to showcase your meal planning creativity. Start by cooking the protein first in a sauté pan or wok using cooking spray or a light coating of oil. Add cut vegetables one by one, starting with those that need a little more cooking time. Serve over your starch or toss starch directly into the stir-fry at the last minute to give it more flavor. Here are some ideas to get you started:

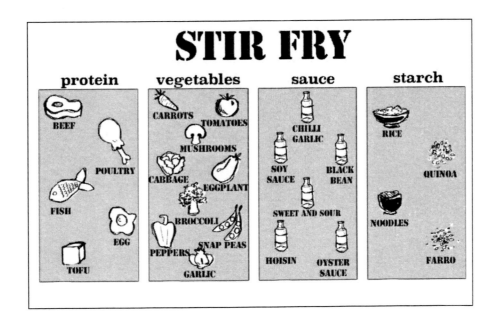

Pasta meals are classic, simple, and almost always a crowd pleaser. When cooking pasta, follow the directions on the package, set the timer, and add some salt to the water. Look for the following recipes in the REBEL Toolbox:

- One Pot Italian Pasta
- Pasta with Spaghetti Sauce with Parmesan
- Pasta with Vegetables and Italian Dressing
- Pasta with Grilled Vegetables

Pizza is also fun to make at home and allows you to be very creative with what you have on hand. Have you ever been to a great pizza restaurant and salivated at all the inventive combinations? Well, you can be just as daring! Start with a basic pizza crust recipe or make individual pizzas using English muffins, bagels, tortillas, or naan bread. Then top with your favorite sauces, proteins, and vegetables! Want to make your pizza like the Italians do? Just hand crush some Roma tomatoes over the crust, then season with fresh garlic, onion, basil, salt, and pepper.

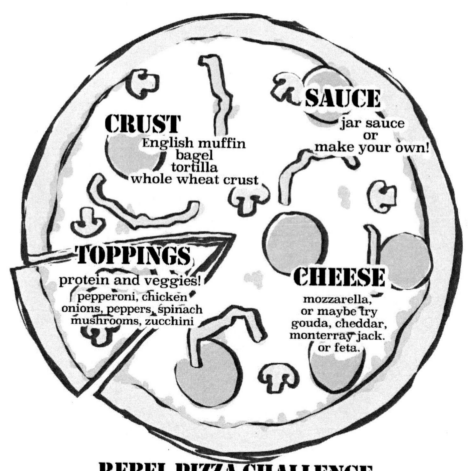

CRUST
English muffin
bagel
tortilla
whole wheat crust

SAUCE
jar sauce
or
make your own!

TOPPINGS
protein and veggies!
pepperoni, chicken
onions, peppers, spinach
mushrooms, zucchini

CHEESE
mozzarella,
or maybe try
gouda, cheddar,
monterray jack.
or feta.

REBEL PIZZA CHALLENGE
Try making a pizza by using a local cheese,
or a vegetable that is in season!

For more great dinner ideas, including recipes for chicken, beef, turkey, seafood, salads, and vegetarian options, visit the REBEL Toolbox.

Come up with seven new dinner recipes to try over the new few weeks. Include ingredients you need or restaurant if eating away from home:

	Menu Items	Groceries Needed or Restaurant
Monday		
Tuesday		
Wednesday		
Thursday		
Friday		
Saturday		
Sunday		

Build a REBELLIOUS Snack!

As mentioned previously, if you combine items with carbohydrates, proteins, and fats, you will avoid swings in your blood sugar, helping you to stay satisfied longer while providing your body with better nutrition. Snacking also helps you pace your food intake throughout the day, preventing you from overeating at your next meal.

Some simple combinations include:

- Beanito® bean chips with fresh salsa
- Roasted chickpeas with olive oil, salt, and paprika
- Turkey pepperoni and crackers
- Carrots, celery, or apples with peanut butter
- String cheese or cheese wedge with rice cakes
- Whole grain tortilla chips and guacamole
- Pretzel chips and hummus
- Tuna or chicken salad and pita chips
- Cottage cheese and fruit
- Greek yogurt with fruit or chocolate chips
- Apple slices and almonds
- Fruit and cheese kabobs

What are some carbohydrate with protein or fat combinations that would work for you as a snack?

Carbohydrate_____ Protein or fat _____

Carbohydrate_____ Protein or fat _____

Carbohydrate_____ Protein or fat _____

Carbohydrate_____ Protein or fat _____

Carbohydrate_____ Protein or fat _____

Now that we have addressed the **what** of eating, we want to help build your confidence by addressing the **when, why, where,** and **how** of eating.

"True kindness has no calories. True kindness is deciding right now that you deserve to feel fabulous." Geneen Roth, *Women, Food and God*

CHAPTER 3: Build Confidence in Your Eating

"Remember, you're the expert when it comes to your body. What works best for one person isn't necessarily right for another." Marsha Hundall, MS, RD, President Green Mountain at Fox Run

What Is Confident Eating?

Many diet programs only address the **what** of eating, labeling foods as "good" or "bad," instructing you to remove certain foods from your diet, and keeping you trapped in diet prison. The **what** of the diet mentality is extremely limiting. In chapter two, you were empowered by the **what** of eating and learned how to eat like a REBEL. On the road to REBELLION, we also need address the *other* aspects of eating: **why, when, where,** and **how**.

Unfortunately, modern society has taken away our natural instincts about eating, and many struggle with the **thoughts, emotions, and behaviors around food**. Think about a toddler; there is almost always a snack bag

within reach that the guardians have with them in the event that their child is hungry. Though it is always accessible, the children are not constantly asking for it or thinking about it unless they are hungry. Unfortunately, this may have been the last time in our lives that we had the ultimate freedom to eat solely based on our bodies' cues. When we were hungry we may have cried. Our caretakers may have tried a nap or a toy or a snack and each time something different satiated us. When we were full, we turned our head, threw the food on the ground, or simply became interested in other things.

Flash forward a few years and we started preschool, grade school, and high school. Our meals became hurried, scheduled, and centered on social events with our friends. When we entered the workforce, lunch may not even be scheduled at all.

Letter from Diet Prison

REBEL Dietitians,
I'm not even sure when I'm hungry anymore or when I'm supposed to eat. Why do I sometimes feel hungry right after I eat or when I get really stressed at work? I rarely get time to have lunch at work and I'm starving when I get home. I find myself eating my way through the kitchen right when I walk in the door. How am I supposed to eat? I don't even know anymore.
-Dieting Darla

POST CARD
Food Police Dept.

PLACE STAMP HERE

Rebel Dietitians
7219 Hanover Prkway
Suite D
Greenbelt, MD
20770

Being a REBEL is standing up for yourself and prioritizing your needs. The challenge is to be bold in a society that is too busy to prioritize the importance of being well-nourished. We will help you find out how to make this work in your own REBELLIOUS way when demand on your time is high and your autonomy with eating is low.

We want you to REBEL against the mechanical aspects of dieting and think of eating as the art of feeding yourself the way that works for you. We have read and digested the research and hope to simplify and inspire your REBELLIOUS path to a healthy and happy relationship with food.

First, it is important to understand two scientifically proven nutrition principles in order to build your confidence in your eating, particularly the **when, why, where,** and **how** of eating: *"intuitive eating"* and *"mindful eating."*

Intuitive Eating: The "When" and "Why" of Eating

REBELs see the concept of intuitive eating as the **when** and **why** of eating. "The underlying premise of Intuitive Eating is (learning) to respond to your inner body cues, because you were born with all the wisdom you need for eating intuitively. 'Eat when you're hungry and stop when you're full' may sound like basic common sense, but when you have a history of chronic dieting or of following rigid 'healthy' rules about eating, it can be quite difficult. To be able to ultimately return to your inborn Intuitive Eater, a number of things need to be in place—most importantly, the ability to trust yourself!"

~Evelyn Tribole, MS, RD and Elyse Resch, MS, RDN, CEDRD, Fiaedp, FADA
The Original Intuitive Eating Pros®

Mindful Eating: The "Where" and "How" of Eating

REBELs see mindful eating as the **where** and **how** of eating. Mindful eating is defined as "eating with intention and attention: eating with the intention of caring for yourself and eating with the attention necessary for noticing and enjoying your food and its effects on your body." Simply put, mindful eating is being "present" with food.

~Michelle May, MD author of *Eat What You Love, Love What You Eat.*

Let's explore how employing the concepts of intuitive eating and mindful eating can help you build confidence in your eating, thus addressing the **when, why, where,** and **how** to eat like a REBEL.

WHEN Are You Eating?

Pay attention to hunger and fullness. How can you REBEL against dieting, learn to eat when you're hungry, and stop when you're full? Life was so much simpler as a toddler when you didn't focus on dieting rules. Hunger was natural and not something that had to be fought or ignored, and fullness was identified without guilt.

On the other hand, dieting teaches us to fight our hunger or to ignore it. One of the questions we ask clients is to describe what hunger feels like to them. We have seen words like *"panic," "emergency,"* and *"pain."* We can probably agree these words all have a negative connotation. There are many reasons that hunger may feel this way. Are you waiting so long to eat that you start feeling physically ill? Did you grow up in food insecurity? Do you fear weight gain? Do you deprive yourself of foods you enjoy? If you can work on getting this feeling of hunger to be neutral and work towards a positive feeling, it will be easier to listen to your body's signals instead of fighting them.

The question often becomes how do you know if you are physically hungry? First, you need to think of where your hunger is coming from. We use all of our senses when it comes to food. The sights, smells, tastes, and even sounds of food can trigger the need to eat. In fact, there are many different types of hunger, and understanding them can help us determine when we are truly physically hungry:

Mouth hunger: *"That tasted amazing; I want more!"*
Head hunger: *"It is noon and time to eat."*
Eye hunger: *"I just saw a commercial for pizza, and now I am so hungry for pizza!"*
Stomach/physical hunger: *"My stomach is grumbling and feels empty."*
Emotional hunger: *"I am sad, and a bowl of ice cream would make me feel better."*

The two types of hunger that are often confused with one another are stomach/physical hunger and emotional hunger. Stomach/physical hunger is a physiological response to the lack of food. The feeling builds gradually, and you may experience a gnawing feeling in the stomach or abdominal area. It is likely to occur several hours after you have last eaten and goes away soon after a meal or snack. On the other hand, emotional hunger develops suddenly and may be perceived as coming from above the neck. Emotional hunger isn't responsive to time after meals and may even persist despite eating and feeling physically full. Emotional hunger is often related to the guilt and shame some people associate with eating.

Satiety. Feeling satisfied can come from a variety of factors. First is physical satiety such as a fullness in your stomach. Pay attention to how you feel when you're finished eating a meal. If you have overeaten, don't punish yourself. Instead, be aware of the physical and/or emotional discomfort that often accompanies being overly full and create a plan to decrease the likelihood that you'll overeat next time. Another piece of the satiety puzzle is choosing food that will not only satisfy your body, but also your mind. Again, it is time to take down the labels of "good" and "bad" and simply give yourself the permission to eat what you want.

Since you may not currently be in tune with your body, you may find it easiest to think of the degree of hunger and fullness using a scale that describes how empty or hungry you feel with the most hungry being "1" and the most full being a "10."

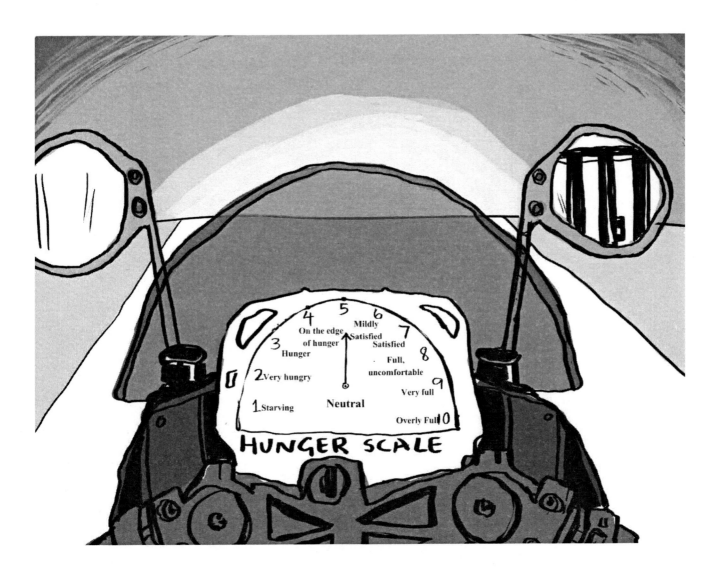

Thinking about and listening to your hunger and fullness are the key you need for the get-away vehicle to transport you far away from the dieting prison. This concept removes the external factors that tell you **why**, **when**, **where**, and **how** to eat that were put in place by the dieting warden, allowing you to claim these decisions as your own. Ride off into the sunset by practicing with the hunger and satiety scale.

Understanding the Hunger and Satiety Scale

1. **Starving:** You feel the negative effects of being overly hungry: headaches, nausea, irritability, and/or lack of concentration. Can you think of a time when you registered a 1? What happened as a result?

   _____

2. **Very hungry:** This is when your thoughts are consumed by food and you find it difficult to concentrate on anything else. For example, as you drive home in traffic from work and pass fast food restaurants, you wrestle with yourself, trying to decide if you are going to stop or if you can wait until you can raid the fridge when you get home. Can you think of a time when you registered a 2? What happened as a result?

   _____

3. **Hunger:** Your stomach may be feeling empty and even rumbling. This would be a good time to eat a meal. Can you think of a time when you registered a 3? What happened as a result?

   _____

4. **On the edge of hunger:** Snack time. You may feel twinges of hunger and know that dinner is not for another 2 to 3 hours. Can you think of a time when you registered a 4? What happened as a result?

   _____

5. **Neutral:** This sensation is often overlooked. Since most people are focusing on hunger and fullness, they may not realize that they are the middle. Can you think of a time when you registered a 5? Did you eat anyway? Can you identify a reason other than hunger that led you to eat?

   _____

6. **Mildly satisfied:** If you were able to look into your stomach, you would see that it is ¾ full. If you tend to eat quickly, we encourage you to pause for a few minutes and reassess your fullness. Did you stay at a 6 or move up to a 7? Can you think of a time when you registered a 6? Did you go back for more?

   _____

7. **Satisfied:** This is fullness and would be a time to pause your eating and see if you continue to feel satisfied. Can you think of a time when you registered a 7? What did you eat?

   _____

8. **Full, uncomfortable:** This is when you have taken a few bites too many. Can you think of a time when you registered an 8? What happened as a result?

   _____

9. **Very full:** This may be the feeling of needing to loosen your belt. Can you think of a time when you registered a 9? What happened as a result?

   _____

10. **Overly full, need to lie down, feeling sick.** Can you think of a time when you registered a 10? What happened as a result?

    _____

One of the best tools for understanding your hunger and fullness is to use a food diary to record where you register on the hunger scale prior to eating and where you fall on the fullness scale after you eat. Logging your mood before and after eating will help you understand what drives your eating in the absence of hunger. Think of trends and reflect on your days as a whole. Do not log calories, points, or grams; instead, log hunger, fullness, and mood before and after meals to help recognize trends. We encourage you to think of eating successes and investigate triggers and emotional eating. Here are some ideas to consider:

- *Did you skip snacks, causing you to overeat at night?*
- *Was your day filled with stress, causing you to eat differently than you normally would?*
- *Did you eat lunch at your desk while checking emails or take it outside for increased enjoyment?*
- *Did you have the same boring dinner every night this week which led to overeating on the weekends simply because you wanted something different?*

Time	Hunger	Mood Before	Food, Amount, and Environment	Satiety	Mood After
ex. 7:00 am	*3*	*Tired*	**Breakfast:** *Toast with peanut butter and banana A glass of milk*	*7*	*Cheery*
			Snack:		
			Lunch:		
			Snack:		
			Dinner:		
			Snack:		

Keep track of your hunger/fullness and mood for a week. Turn to the REBEL Toolbox for a sample of this food log that you can copy and use. Be sure to record any trends you noticed.

_____

_____

_____

_____

Hunger Strike. Frequently in the dieting prison you may be urged to go on a hunger strike to get what you want: weight loss. However, many times mindless eating or overeating first starts with skipping meals. When you skip a meal or go too long in between meals, you are likely to overeat later in the day due to intense physical hunger—quickly bouncing from 1 to 10 on the hunger-satiety scale. The diet mentality says that skipping meals or snacks means "saving" calories to beat the system and lose weight! In reality, the body needs consistent fuel throughout the day. Common scenarios that may develop from skipping meals include:

- Missing breakfast and/or lunch and thinking you saved yourself hundreds of calories! But, when you get home you are so famished, you fall prey to what you have on hand (such as a bag of chips or grazing while preparing dinner). By the time dinner is ready, you are too full to enjoy it and miss out on the nutritious meal you have created.
- Stopping at the drive-thru when you are overly hungry. You can't fathom spending more time to prepare a meal at home. Maybe you are not even hungry for fast food, but that is what is readily available.
- Eating super-sized helpings at dinner or continuing to eat afterward since you have starved all day long.

These things are not inherently "bad," but with the lack of planning you will miss out on the balance and variety that is so important. If you notice this trend in your meal logs, break it down and see where you can infuse awareness into this cycle.

Another common scenario is when people skip breakfast, perhaps due to lack of time before they have to leave for the day or not being hungry first thing in the morning. Often, these same people are eating the bulk of their calories late in the day, so it's no wonder they are not hungry before they leave for work in the morning! If this describes you, try eating something every three to four hours until your body is back on a regular cycle. Then you can focus on eating intuitively. Once you start eating breakfast, you may be surprised to feel your hunger normalizing throughout the day. This is your inner REBEL waking up! Now you can honor this hunger and fuel your body as the day goes on. YOU are in charge of when to eat, not the diet.

Before your next meal, ask yourself:

1. What type of hunger do I have: physical, emotional, or other? _____
2. When was the last time I had a meal or snack? _____
3. Will eating help meet my hunger? (Yes, no, or not sure) _____

WHY Are You Eating?

Now, let's focus on the next step in trusting and nurturing belief in your body. Understanding **why** you are eating (in a curious and non-judgmental way) is just as important as knowing **what** to eat and **when**. So, what should you do if you register a "5" or above on the hunger-fullness scale and determine that hunger is not present? Can you think of **why** you are eating?

> **"Practice being curious about and compassionate with your emotions.**
> **If you slip into judgment, use mindfulness to notice this happened and**
> **return to curiosity and compassion."** Karen R. Koenig, LCSW, MEd

Emotional Eating

Here are the six common emotions that lead to emotional eating. Can you think of times when these emotions triggered you to eat when you were not hungry?

Anger: Anger is an uncomfortable emotion to feel so you avoid it, distract from it, and run from it. When you are angry at yourself or another person, eating can be a way to avoid conflict. When you feel that you are not being heard, whether it is in a relationship or at work/school, you may try to comfort yourself with food. Food doesn't talk back, food is always available, and food doesn't judge. Some foods may even have a chemically soothing effect. Short term, this may feel helpful, but ultimately, eating to calm yourself takes you further away from your health goals.

 Write down some times when you felt angry, causing you to eat when you were not hungry:

_____

_____

Stress: Stress can be physical, mental, or emotional, and eating may seem to temporarily relieve these chaotic feelings by providing a moment of relaxation. While eating you are able to put your stress on the side and enjoy a moment of peace. Over the long term, however, your body's flight or fight mechanism was not designed to eat while under stress, preferring to take care of the "emergency" at hand. Therefore, eating while under stress can also exacerbate digestive diseases such as ulcers, gastric reflux, irritable bowel syndrome, etc.

 Write down some times when you felt stressed, causing you to eat when you were not hungry:

_____

_____

DEPRIVATION

Deprivation: When you classify foods as good or bad, you assign the food power. These word games can fuel your desire for the "bad" foods, resulting in a binge. For example, if a diet says that the secret to lasting weight loss is that you should never eat pizza again, you would probably start fantasizing about pizza. Eventually, this constant dreaming about forbidden foods takes on a life of its own, and you may begin to binge on "forbidden" foods (often in secret), ultimately ramping up the guilt and negative feelings about being a "failure."

Write down some times when you felt deprived, causing you to eat when you were not hungry:

_____

_____

BOREDOM

Boredom: When you increase awareness, you may find that you eat when you are bored. You mindlessly munch on pretzels to get through a meeting at work. You drive through the fast food take-out line for a shake or fries just to fill a void between appointments. Or, you grab the chips and dip while watching television. Boredom also results from eating the same foods repeatedly. Just like deprivation, eating the same thing day after day is bound to stimulate desire for foods you feel you can no longer eat—again, paving the way to feelings of failure for venturing "off the plan."

Write down some times when you were bored, causing you to eat when you were not hungry:

_____

_____

FATIGUE

Fatigue: Contrary to candy bar commercials on TV, eating doesn't automatically equal an energy burst. While food does naturally provide energy throughout the day, it doesn't help if you're not hungry. In fact, people who do not get enough sleep actually produce less *leptin* (the hormone that tells us to stop eating) and more *ghrelin* (the hormone that tells us to eat more) than those who get enough rest. This cycle of fatigue and eating is complicated by the fact that if you overeat (such as when you eat when tired), you actually feel more tired!

Write down some times when you were tired, causing you to eat when you were not hungry:

_____

_____

Failure: Feelings of failure can happen to any of us at any time. Did you miss a deadline at work or forget an appointment at your child's school, then soothe those guilty feelings with a snack? How about when you go to buy clothes, but you don't like what you see in the mirror? Do you head for the nearest chocolate bar? In fact, failure usually sets in just after breaking a diet rule. At this point you may be feeling, "I messed up. What is the point anyway?" and finish out the day "off the wagon" with new resolve to start over the next day.

Write down some times when you felt like a failure, causing you to eat when you were not hungry:

_____

_____

"Dieting and deprivation actually create feelings of failure, depression, anxiety about eating, self-loathing, and (eventually lead to) more emotional eating."
Sumner Brooks, RD *Savvy Girl A Guide to Eating*

You are not alone if you find yourself driven to eat in response to emotions. This is a part of normal eating. The key is to decrease the frequency in which this occurs and add more tools to your toolbox so you can cope with these emotions. The more you are aware of your triggers, the better equipped you will be to use these new tools.

If you are struggling with feelings of depression or anxiety, we encourage you to seek the advice of a mental health professional to complement your work with your REBEL Dietitian®.

WHERE Are You Eating?

Being a REBEL means becoming aware of your body (inside and out), feeling your feelings, and understanding why you are eating so you can set up your healthy eating environment. Understanding **where** you are eating is the next step in *Tasting the Sweet REBELLION*.

Take some time to think about this. **Where** do you eat meals? Are you by yourself? In the car? With family? With a co-worker? In front of the television? It is important to eat where you can savor your meals whenever possible.

"It is difficult to eat a balanced meal when you are literally trying to balance it on your lap."
Rebecca Bitzer, MS, RD, LD, CEDRD

REBEL At Home

When was the last time you took 30 minutes to eat dinner either alone or with your family? Eating at the table helps you to relax, eat more slowly, and may provide other benefits including maintenance of healthier body weights. Even if you eat alone, eating slowly at the table provides a better environment for you to focus on your hunger and fullness cues.

To make mealtimes more enjoyable, we encourage you to try some of the following:

- Setting the table with festive décor and using the "fancy" tableware even if it is not a holiday.
- Eating by candlelight (use unscented candles so they don't distract from the aroma of your meal).
- Playing some soothing music.
- Plating your food carefully with attention to detail including edible garnishes and serving a variety of color and food combinations.
- Turning off phones, tablets, and game consoles.
- Choosing positive "table topics" that can add enjoyment to the meal.

By taking the time to create this meal experience, you will likely be more mindful and enjoy eating, ultimately limiting overindulging or excess snacking later that night.

Did You Know?

The emotional benefits of spending time together over a meal causes children to:

- Be three times less likely to use marijuana
- Be two times less likely to drink alcohol
- Achieve better test scores

In addition, children who eat dinner at the table with their families:

- Maintain healthier body weights
- Limit their TV time
- Get enough sleep
- Are more confident

Try eating your snacks at the table (at work or at home) this week. What did you notice?

_____

_____

_____

_____

REBEL Eating Outside of the Home

Don't let weight or food concerns prevent you from enjoying life and attending fun events. If your eating preferences or stress and guilt about food keep you isolated, it is imperative that you begin working on your relationship with food. The goal is to find enjoyment again as you take part in traditional and social food situations! Here are some REBEL Tips to help you navigate various scenarios:

Restaurants: Pick the type of food you are hungry for, and see how you can make it fit into a complete meal. Remember to balance carbohydrates, protein, and fat. For example, are you hungry for pasta? Order a pasta entrée with chicken or fish for some protein and include a side salad. Remember to stop halfway through the meal and check your hunger and fullness cues. Or, do you love the bread they serve before the meal? Have a piece or two and savor it. Then, make the bulk of your dinner a protein item such as chicken or fish with vegetables.

Holiday Meals: Don't skip meals in preparation for the main event; rather, fuel yourself with small meals or healthy snacks throughout the day. Survey all the foods and pick your favorites. Do you only get your mom's homemade stuffing or your grandma's special macaroni and cheese once a year? Definitely go for your favorites and think twice about more generic sides like frozen corn or boxed mashed potatoes—foods you can have all year round any time you please. Make sure to stop periodically during the day to check in with yourself. Ask the questions, "*How am I feeling? Am I hungry?*" We encourage you to write a positive quote on an index card and keep it with you during dinner to look at if you're feeling overwhelmed. Another idea is to wear a shiny bracelet that can serve as a reminder to check in with yourself when you see it.

Happy Hour: This type of event can be tricky. Is it dinner? Is it a snack? The answer is whatever you need it to be. If it's an earlier time than you would normally eat, be flexible and eat what you are hungry for, then fill the gaps at home. Typically, happy hour food includes a variety of appetizers and pub food. Consider making a plate for yourself with your favorites. Try not to eat directly off of the serving plates, since it can be too hard to judge portion sizes and total intake without the visual of a personal plate.

Dinner Party: Do you get overwhelmed when someone invites you over and you start thinking, "*What if they serve things I shouldn't eat?*" Again, take a breath and change your mindset. Bring some positivity to the situation and tell yourself that you are going to have a fun night where you don't have to cook! Likely this is not happening every night of the week. The most important thing to remember is that one meal is not going to make or break you. Perhaps the host is only serving pasta and bread—no protein and no vegetables. What are you to do? Simply savor the food, eat slowly, enjoy the company, and remember there are many more dinners to be had this week!

Drive Thru: Life is busy and the convenience of fast food may play an occasional part in helping you manage your schedule. Then again, perhaps you really enjoy certain fast foods. There is no set number of times a week, month, or year that these foods are recommended. The best way to decide what is best for you is to consider how often you eat drive thru foods now. The reason for moderation is that these foods are typically low in fruits and vegetables, lean protein, heart healthy fats, and fiber. Many times fast food is the complete opposite of mindful eating. Maybe you are running late for an event and trying to grab dinner on the run. At this point, your mind is focused on everything you have to do—making all the green lights, following directions, helping the kids get situated in the back of the car, and finishing eating before you reach your destination or before you have to merge with the highway. Aside from not being able to safely drive and eat, this eliminates your ability to eat mindfully. So even though fast food is often high in sugar, sodium, and fat, you might not even taste it because you are distracted by everything else. As an alternative, try eating at the table in the restaurant or at home with your family. (If you are prone to eating on the way home, ask someone else to pick up the food for you.) If you love the spicy chicken sandwich (grains and protein), pair it with a side salad and a piece of fruit so you can cover half your plate with fruits and vegetables. Or, if you love French fries, make them a part of a well-balanced meal by also eating a chicken entrée salad. It doesn't have to be all or nothing.

"Don't let food get in the way of what really matters." Kait Fortunato, RD, LD

HOW Are You Eating?

Being a REBEL means allowing yourself to enjoy food in any environment and being flexible in an unpredictable world. Now that you can think of **what, when, why,** and **where** you are eating, let's take some time to practice **how** to savor the foods you are eating.

If you are not paying attention to the food you are eating, it will leave you unsatisfied and wanting more. We would love to share with you some tips on how to SAVOR the foods you are eating. We encourage you to use these techniques to give yourself permission to taste your food—think of a toddler whose face gets covered with spaghetti sauce as she explores and plays with her food. We can help you embrace the food that you are eating, allowing for more joy and contentment from your meals.

Food is not the enemy, and it is perfectly fine to love food. Loving food does not mean overeating; however, it means taking the time to enjoy each bite. Although the food is almost always blamed, it is really **how** we are eating that we want to fine-tune. Imagine that eating is like wine tasting—learn about it, hold it up so you can see it, smell it, sip a small mouthful, think of the taste, and describe the flavors. It is about SAVORING the foods you enjoy and slowing down so you can concentrate on the enjoyment of eating while letting your internal hunger and fullness guide you about how much you eat.

Putting It into Practice

Eat without distractions. Are you guilty of mindlessly eating while talking on the phone, browsing the Internet, or watching television? These distractions take can take you away from truly appreciating your meals. These habits may also distract you from checking in with your hunger and fullness cues.

We encourage you to practice eating your meals and snacks at the table. If you are busy watching TV and are *physically* hungry, you will make the effort to get up to have a snack. However, if you are *not* hungry, it will seem like a nuisance to actually stop what you are doing, go to the table, and eat. Eating at the table also allows for tasting and savoring your meals. Distractions will dilute the enjoyment of your food and make it difficult to determine fullness. For example, have you ever gotten sucked into social media or a conversation with a co-worker only to look down and find your plate is clean? You may not remember eating. You certainly didn't taste the food. And you may even want more! Being present with your meal will not only help you taste it, but it contributes to the feeling of satisfaction we all want after a meal.

Practice these steps to master your awareness of eating and *Taste the Sweet REBELLION:*

1. Take a few deep breaths. Leave your stressors behind and become present with your food.
2. Ask yourself what you are hungry for:
   - *What texture? (crunchy, soft, chewy, creamy, smooth, crispy)*
   - *What taste? (salty, sweet, savory, spicy, sour)*
   - *What temperature? (piping hot, warm, chilled, ice cold)*
3. Set the table and plate your food.
4. Spend a minute investigating your plate. Use your sense of smell to appreciate the aroma, play with your food and touch it, listen to the crunch of your food, and take in the visual of your plate.
5. Taste your food. How does it feel on your tongue? What descriptive words come to mind? If you notice that you are not enjoying what you chose, choose something else if possible.
6. See the REBEL Toolbox for a list of food adjectives. Describe your food to someone as if they have never seen it before.
7. Pause in the middle of eating for at least two full minutes. Determine where you fall on the hunger and satiety scale.

Eating Styles

Below is a list of "eating styles." Is there one in particular that describes you? Or, are there pieces of each you can relate to? Thinking of how you eat can help you brainstorm positive changes toward happy, healthy eating:

1. **Chaotic Eaters:** These eaters tend to be extremely busy or not comfortable with food preparation and cooking and therefore rely mainly on convenience foods. Meal planning is not one of their strengths, and they may wait too long to eat.
   Positive: Chaotic eaters do not spend much time planning meals, so this is a stressor they don't feel.
   Negative: Chaotic eaters may feel tired throughout the day because they have not been fueling their bodies consistently.
   Tip: Add "eat lunch," "meal plan," and "grocery shop" as appointments on your calendar so you remember. Make these appointments as important as meetings for work or a doctor's appointment. They are tasks you need to do to take care of yourself.

2. **Emotional Eaters:** These eaters often overuse food as a coping mechanism. They may overeat or crave specific foods in times of sadness, stress, or even happiness. Hunger and fullness cues are sometimes ignored.
   Positive: Emotional eaters feel comfort and stress reduction in the short term.
   Negative: Emotional eaters often suffer guilt after episodes of emotional eating, leading to more eating for comfort.
   Tip: See Chapter 4 for more self-care ideas.

3. **Convenience Eaters:** These eaters primarily choose quickly prepared foods including a majority of processed foods. They will stop at convenience stores and fast food restaurants on their way home because they have not been grocery shopping. Rarely using their kitchen to cook or eat, convenience eaters may try to eat healthy, but this may be difficult given the options available.

   Positive: Since convenience eaters don't plan meals or eat much at home, they have one less thing on their to-do list.

   Negative: Convenience eaters often fall victim to the foods that are available at that moment and may not eat foods they are really hungry for.

   Tip: Aim to eat at least one homemade meal a week. Slowly try to eat more meals from home.

4. **Chronic Dieters:** People with diet mentalities often group foods into "good" and "bad" food lists. They may deprive themselves of favorite foods that do not fall within the current plan they are on. We see extreme eating habits in people with a diet mentality—they are either 100% on a diet or 100% off a diet. There is no happy medium, and they are often preoccupied with food, calories, grams, and weight.

   Positive: People with a diet mentality are well-read on nutrition.

   Negative: People with a diet mentality often have too much information, making it difficult to make nutrition choices that address all of the "rules." Mealtime is generally stressful.

   Tip: Incorporate favorite foods into your weekly plan while paying attention to balance and portions.

5. **Munchers**: These people usually do not sit down for a full breakfast, lunch, or dinner. Instead, they tend to snack throughout the day on whatever is available. When munchers are making dinner, they often snack and taste test while cooking; therefore, their hunger and fullness cues may not be in tune.

   Positive: Munchers fuel themselves throughout the day with snacks.

   Negative: Munchers are not in tune with their hunger or fullness and may over- or under-eat, missing out on the balanced nutrition their body needs.

   Tip: Aim to have set meals and snacks for one day and see how you feel!

6. **Selective Eaters**: These people have a very limited food selection. They usually eat the same thing every day and may be afraid to try new foods.

   Positive: Selective eaters know what they like to eat, so meal planning and grocery shopping takes very little time.

   Negative: Selective eaters have very little variety in their diet and may be lacking nutrients or missing out on social eating for fear they will not be able to eat anything provided.

   Tip: It takes time to figure out if you like a food. Some experts say you need at least 20 exposures. You may like a food and not even know it, so keep trying.

7. **REBEL Eaters:** REBELs use hunger and fullness signals to decide when it is time to eat. They eat foods they are hungry for, listening to their bodies' wants and needs. They eat in social situations without feeling guilty.

   Positive: REBEL eaters are in tune with their hunger and fullness signals most of the time.

   Negative: This process takes practice.

   Tip: Stick with it and use your REBEL workbook to guide you.

Meet REBEL Client Mike (a Chaotic and Convenient Eater)

Mike is a middle-aged, single man who works as a plumber. He spends most of his time on the road, driving between house calls. He eats lunch and sometimes dinner at a local fast food chain every day. In order to keep up with his busy schedule, he often goes through the drive thru and devours his burger and French fries in less than five minutes. Mike asked for help with healthier eating. He didn't like how tired he felt all day long.

Through our sessions, Mike began to pinpoint some specific eating behaviors that may be causing his lack of energy. He realized he had qualities of both a chaotic and convenience eater, so we worked on setting small meal planning goals to manage his hunger and the logistics of his eating schedule. One of Mike's assignments included eating a peanut butter sandwich for breakfast—even if he had to eat it as he was walking out the door. When he ate at the fast food restaurant for lunch, he agreed to spend at least 10 minutes eating his burger as opposed to quickly devouring the meal all at once. As Mike was eating his meal, he realized he truly enjoyed the taste of the burgers and fries. He felt very satisfied that day after both his breakfast and lunch. During the day, he noted he felt less fatigued, and more ready to finish up the rest of his tasks. Being mindful about **what, where, why,** and **how** he was eating helped Mike make food choices that he enjoyed and kept him full during the day. Over time, Mike even began to incorporate a wider variety of foods.

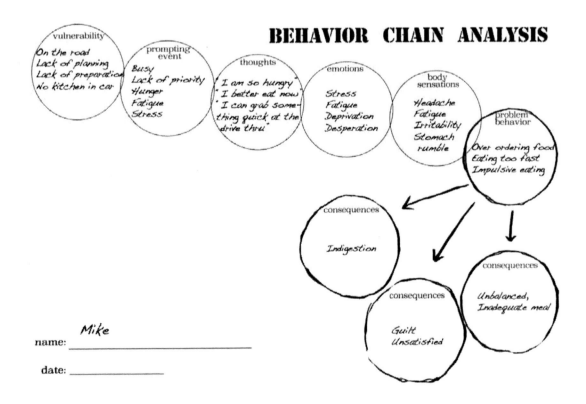

Now, fill out your own behavior chain based on your eating styles!

name: _____

date: _____

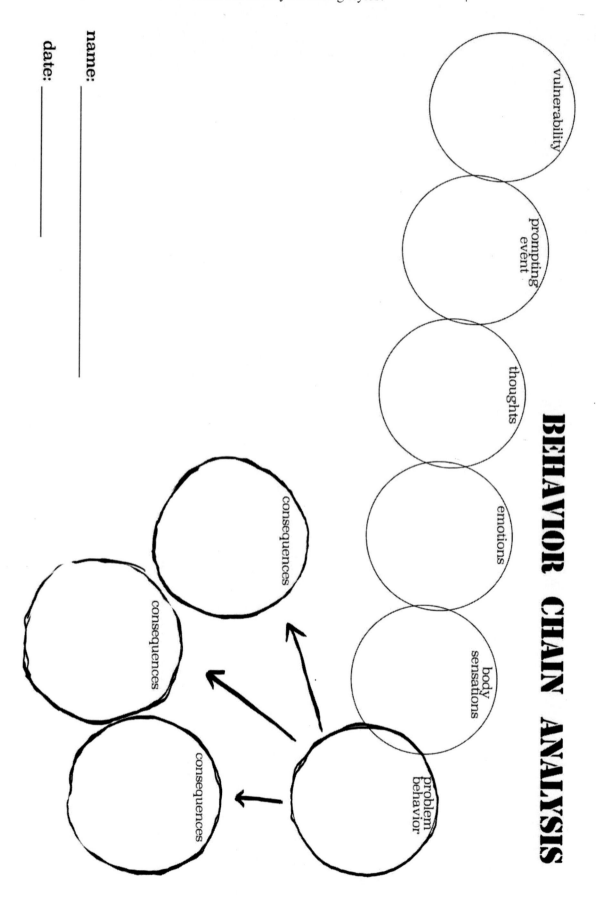

BEHAVIOR CHAIN ANALYSIS

vulnerability

prompting event

thoughts

emotions

body sensations

problem behavior

consequences

consequences

consequences

As you become a more confident eater, there are small changes you can make to set yourself up for success. As REBEL Dietitians®, we see everything as a process. We want you to be healthy AND happy no matter what. How can you empower yourself to resist diets, eat like a REBEL, and build confidence in your eating?

_____

_____

_____

_____

_____

_____

_____

_____

_____

_____

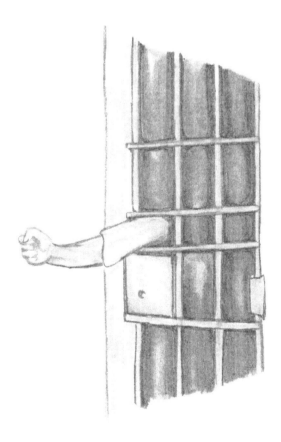

CHAPTER 4: Empower Yourself

You can spend your whole life fighting your weight,
or you can spend your life living." Dana Magee, RD, LD, CLT

Escaping Diet Prison

The ultimate goal of this workbook is to help you map your escape from diet prison—identify the trigger and break free, understand the allure and stomp it out, end the restriction, and abolish the guilt. When imprisoned, you were told what and when to eat and now **you** get to be in charge.

Prison takes away your individuality. You may have been locked in for a few weeks, months, years, or even decades, but the key to unlocking your freedom and finding your inner REBEL is to make yourself a priority and value your own health and happiness. The triggers, allure, restriction, and guilt will always be waiting for you on the other side of the bars, but you don't need to go back there. Taking care of yourself will empower you to stay motivated to do the grocery shopping, the planning, the prepping, and the work that goes into improving both your nutrition and your relationship with food.

Letter from Diet Prison

REBEL Dietitians,

I don't even know what's important to me anymore. I feel so confused by all this conflicting information. I am surrounded by diet paraphernalia and feel more overwhelmed that I ever have. The days are mundane, I am hardly getting any sleep.

-Dieting Darla

POST CARD
Food Police Dept.

PLACE STAMP HERE

Rebel Dietitians
72l9 Hanover Prkway
Suite D
Greenbelt, MD
20770

Rebuild Your Life Around Your Values as You Break Out of Diet Prison

Unlike a goal, a value is never-ending—something you will do for the rest of your life. For example, a goal is to get married; whereas, a value is to have a loving relationship. A goal is to lose weight, and a value is to have a healthy relationship with food. If you have been out of touch with your body while you followed diet after diet, it's going to take some time to snuff out your diet mentality and begin to rebuild your life around what is truly important to you. Dieting replaces your individual voice and values with perfection, control, and discipline. Dieting brought you further away from your values, and REBELLING will bring them back in the spotlight.

How can we move forward if we aren't even sure what we personally value? What do you consider a priority now that you have ditched the diet?

_____

_____

_____

_____

_____

_____

What Are Your Values?

Circle any of those below that are meaningful to you. See the examples for some ideas of how the REBEL approach can bring you closer to these values. These values will greatly impact not only your food choices but the **when, why, where,** and **how** of your eating. Try to focus on what you *feel* as opposed to what you *think* you should value. There will be no judgment!

REBEL Values (Adapted from mindtools.com)

Accountability (To yourself or your treatment team)	**Enjoyment** (Such as enjoying the taste of food)	**Leadership** (Such as being a role model for other REBELs)
Achievement (Such as ditching the diet for GOOD)	**Structure** (Such as planning themed meals for the week and buying appropriate groceries)	**Love** (Such as eating meals with the people you love)
Adventurousness (Such as trying new foods or restaurants)	**Hard Work** (Such as putting in the time necessary to change your health behaviors)	**Positivity** (Such as how you feel about your body)
Balance (Such as practicing moderation)	**Family Oriented** (Such as eating meals with your family)	**Serenity** (Such as making peace with food and your body)
Elegance (Such as setting the table before meals)	**Independence** (Such as boldly making your own food choices)	**Spontaneity** (Such as being flexible with food choices)
Economy (Such as trying to use the groceries you buy instead of letting them go bad)	**Effectiveness** (Such as finding what works for you in terms of health and nutrition)	**Strength** (Such as the ability to resist diet temptations)
Happiness (Such as eliminating the stress that used to surround eating)	**Determination** (Such as not losing sight of what truly makes you happy)	**Support** (Such as asking for help when you need it)
Commitment (Such as committing to being a REBEL and staying free of diet prison)	**Freedom** (Such as being free from the diet prison)	**Teamwork** (Such as getting your family involved in meal preparation)
Improvement (Such as taking small steps towards health and happiness)	**Creativity** (Such as making a body positive collage)	**Trustworthiness** (Such as learning to trust your body to stop you from eating when you are full)
Compassion (Toward others or yourself)	**Growth** (Such as navigating from diet prison to a REBEL eating mentality)	**Uniqueness** (Such as going against the grain and REBELLING against diets)
Cooperation (Such as cooking or shopping with others)	**Health** (In both body and mind)	**Fun** (Such as having ice cream with a friend)

Now, take some of the values that you have circled. Fill out the chart below with how dieting has stood in the way of this value, and how being a REBEL can help you work towards aligning your life with your values.

Value	How did dieting stand in the way of this value?	How does REBELLING promote this value?
ex. Being adventurous	Being very rigid with the foods I eat, not open to experiencing new things.	Going out to dinner with a friend and trying something new!
ex. Family time	Because I eat different foods than my family, I spend more time cooking for myself instead of sitting at the table and enjoying a meal with them.	Cook a meal that incorporates food that my family and I can enjoy together.

You have identified what is important to you, and now it is time to bring these values back into your life. This next section will help you combine your own values with the knowledge, or "street smarts," to help you get and stay out of diet prison. You will never have to be a repeat offender in the diet world! Combining your values, expanding your nutrition knowledge, redefining health, and practicing self-care will be your "get out of jail free card." See more information about using your values to guide you in our REBEL Toolbox.

"Street Smarts"

Knowledge is power. Now that you are free, let's keep your independence from diets by arming yourself with knowledge so the negatives of dieting don't creep back in. Use this information to counter any allure from diets, as they WILL present themselves. Diets turn you against yourself. Dieting fights your body's natural processes. Knowing more about how your body works and why you are the way you are will help you see through the false promises of dieting.

Knowing Your Genetics

It is important to realize that genetics play a huge role in your body size, shape, weight, and metabolism. There is a long road between *knowing* that some things are out of your control and finding *acceptance* in your body.

Effects of Genetics on Weight and Metabolism

- 50–80% of weight is determined by genes.
- 40–70% of BMI (Body Mass Index—the relationship between your height and weight) is determined by your genes.
- Distribution of fat on your body is 40% genetic.
- 40–80% of RMR (Resting Metabolic Rate—how many calories your body burns at rest just sitting in a chair powering your brain, heart, liver, kidneys and other essential functions such as breathing) is genetic.

Know Your Metabolism

Part of the allure of many diets is a promise to "boost your metabolism." But, what exactly is metabolism? And can diets actually "boost" it?

The term metabolism is "the breakdown of food and its transformation into energy." Your body needs calories, even at rest, in order to survive. The majority of your daily caloric needs is used to fuel your essential organs including your heart, kidneys, lungs, and brain.

Feeding your body consistently is the best way to stimulate your metabolism, whereas dieting is one of the culprits that can slow your metabolism. In fact, just 24 to 48 hours of food restriction can decrease your metabolic rate by 15 to 30%. Not only does your body need a lot more calories than is allotted on a typical diet (even *without* exercise), but cutting these calories will also damage your metabolism. Knowing this can help you resist those extreme calorie-cutting diets.

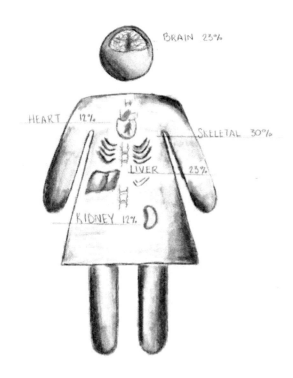

The majority of your daily caloric needs is used to fuel your essential organs.

Knowing Your Set Point

We know that weight loss is still important to a lot of people, so let's talk about it. Remember, you have natural mechanisms in your body that tell you when and how much to eat. It is possible that we may have lost it over the years through different diets that encouraged us to ignore it. When you stop trying to control your weight through willpower, your body starts doing the job for you. Your "set point" is defined as the healthy weight that your body aims for—the weight you maintain when you listen and respond to your body's signals of hunger and fullness.

Your body likes to maintain the status quo and keep your weight relatively stable; this range of stable weight is called your "setpoint."
Linda Bacon, PhD, author *Health at Every Size: The Surprising Truth About Your Weight*

Once you're able to *Taste the Sweet REBELLION* by feeling confident in your food choices, listening to your body's signals, and beginning to live by your true values, your body will find your set point weight.

What if your BMI is outside of the "normal" range? Did you know BMI was actually created for life insurance purposes in the early 19th century? It was never intended to measure the individual but to be used in population studies, therefore there are limitations to BMI. It does not take into account muscle tone or build, nor does it pay attention to individual growth trends, age, race, ethnicity, or gender. Even some professional athletes who are otherwise perceived as the epitome of health and fitness could be labeled overweight or obese.

Remember, changes in weight are normal and expected as you age. During puberty, weight gain is expected for normal growth; however, if misunderstood, this gain can trigger dieting behavior. Interestingly enough, the same information that was used to create the BMI table also shows that the average women gains about 20 pounds within the 40 years from age 20 to 60. Weight gain throughout the life cycle is *normal* and *expected*.

Avoid Being a Repeat Offender

Armed with knowledge about your body, you can avoid being a repeat offender. Now it is time to empower yourself by setting up your environment to support your new REBEL lifestyle. You no longer need the mementos of diets past waiting to trigger you into their prison. It might be scary at first to be on the outside, but you will soon love the freedom that being a REBEL provides. Here are some steps to take to ensure you will not fall victim to dieting ever again:

Step 1. Get rid of the scale. It is amazing how much control one piece of equipment can have over our lives. In order to truly recognize self-worth, it's time to stop measuring your value based on the number on the scale. This may be very frightening and overwhelming. If so, start small. Put the scale in the bathroom closet. Only weigh yourself every other day or once a week. Eventually, your REBEL mindset will kick in, and you'll be able to get rid of your scale.

Smash the scale. Rip up the BMI chart. Start living like a REBEL!

Below are examples of common diet mentality thoughts based on the number on the scale:

Diet thought: *"If I don't weigh myself, I will go off the deep end and gain a bunch of weight."*
REBEL thought: You will know that you are taking care of yourself when you have lasting energy, are sleeping throughout the night, and are eating the foods you love without fear or guilt.

Diet thought: *"If my weight is down, I am doing a good job."*
REBEL thought: Many times we think that seeing a lower number on the scale will serve as motivation or a reward for a job well done. Be careful about heading down this road. We have seen it turn into "*I did a good job and now I deserve a reward.*" That person then eats food they were not hungry for. Or, "*I must be super careful today so that number does not go back up.*" This can lead to further restriction and extreme hunger in the end.

Diet thought: *"If my weight is up, who cares anymore?"*
REBEL thought: When the weight is down it messes with our psyche and when the weight is up it messes with our psyche. In reality those with healthy body weights do fluctuate. This is normal and expected. It is when we allow our weight to affect our eating that we get into trouble, and this fluctuation turns into a trend. Focusing on the weight makes it near impossible to eat intuitively, and we are once again focused on an external factor that tells us how much to eat.

Step 2: Get rid of diet paraphernalia. In order to improve your body acceptance, you have to craft an environment for success. A decrease in acceptance of your body can occur from:

Magazines that discuss the latest diet trends or weight-loss stunt. Every time you open these magazines you may feel triggered by the various claims. Seeing edited images may also cause you to start comparing yourself to others.

Calorie counting apps on your tablets or phone. If counting calories becomes a stressor in your life, it is time to ditch it. For some people it becomes a point of obsession, leading to guilt which can drive emotional eating. Sometimes with calorie driven apps we find our clients are still hungry at the end of the day, but they have "used up" their allotted calories and either stop eating or feel guilty for eating. Clients may also have a day where they have 300 calories left and eat for the sole reason that it is "allowed," even in the absence of hunger.

Social media platforms. Unfortunately, there are endless diet-related messages on social media. These forms of interactive media are such a huge part of our lives today, it may be impractical to cut them out completely. But, you can take charge over the pages and people you follow on social media. For example, consider blocking the pages and people who post triggering images and replace them with positive body websites. It may also be helpful to limit the time you spend browsing and interacting on social media.

Measuring cups and food scales. When used for "exact" portioning and weighing of food, measuring cups and food scales dilute the joy of plating your meal. Use our handy portions in Chapter 2 as a guide to get started and allow your hunger and fullness to do the rest.

Trash the diet paraphernalia you have in your house and see how empowered you feel. Always ask yourself, "Is this bringing me closer to or further away from rebuilding the life I want to live?"

Step 3: Say "no" to food pushers. Food pressures to eat more or less can often get in the way of eating according to your personal hunger cues. Remember no one else knows your level of hunger and what your body needs. It is important that *you* decide if, how much, what, and when you are eating. Many times "food pushers" will ask you to finish up something because they "made it for you," "spent all day working on it," or "made it because it was your favorite." A firm "no" can be difficult to muster when you fear hurting their feelings. We would suggest:

- Start with a polite "*No, thank you.*"
- Still receiving resistance? Reassure them, "*It looks or smells delicious, but I am full.*" Ask to take some home to eat later when you become hungry again.
- Still receiving the third degree? Is this someone you can be honest with? Tell them that it is important for you to make your own decisions regarding food. Or, take a single, "polite bite" to keep the peace. Remember this is just one meal, and one meal will not have an overall impact on your health. It will be important to discuss your feelings with this person at another time.

Step 4. Prioritize self-care. When you are running yourself ragged and not taking care of yourself, you can become a repeat offender of the dieting prison. Take time each day to do something small that makes you feel good about yourself, brings you joy, and relieves both chronic and acute stressors. It is imperative for a healthy life that you practice self-care regularly, not just when you are feeling the effects of a busy life. If you take care of yourself all month, you will be ready to face those days when you get slammed with new work projects or personal stress.

Let's think of ways you can soothe yourself without turning to food when hunger is not the reason you are searching the fridge or pantry. We encourage you to keep a self-care checklist to make sure this component is being filled on a daily basis. Whether it takes five minutes or two hours, it is important to incorporate some sort of self-care each day.

Self-Care Checklist

- ❏ Learn a new skill
- ❏ Take a bath
- ❏ Listen to music
- ❏ Visit a museum or art gallery
- ❏ Go for a walk
- ❏ Practice yoga or meditate
- ❏ Relax outside
- ❏ Relax in a whirlpool or sauna
- ❏ Say or read a spiritual prayer
- ❏ Practice deep breathing
- ❏ Concentrate on a relaxing scene
- ❏ Create a collage that represents the "real you"
- ❏ Receive a massage
- ❏ Get a hair-cut
- ❏ Attend a favorite athletic event
- ❏ Do something adventurous
- ❏ Do a crossword puzzle
- ❏ Go dancing
- ❏ Play a musical instrument
- ❏ Plan an at-home spa day (robe, cucumbers on eyes, lotions, etc.)
- ❏ Garden and work with plants
- ❏ Learn a new skill
- ❏ See a special play, movie, or concert
- ❏ Go on a picnic in a beautiful setting

- ❏ Ride a bicycle
- ❏ Draw or paint a picture
- ❏ Make a list of your goals for the future
- ❏ Swim and relax at the beach or pool
- ❏ Visit a special place you enjoy
- ❏ Volunteer at a shelter
- ❏ Sit in front of a fireplace
- ❏ Read a comic or joke book
- ❏ Watch a cartoon
- ❏ Write a letter to an old friend
- ❏ Play at an amusement park
- ❏ Count your blessings
- ❏ Play as you did as a child
- ❏ Window shop
- ❏ Reward yourself with a gift you can afford
- ❏ Take yourself on vacation
- ❏ Create with clay or pottery
- ❏ Pet/play with an animal
- ❏ Write a poem
- ❏ Get a pedicure and/or manicure
- ❏ Make a bouquet of flowers
- ❏ Create a scrapbook
- ❏ Call an old friend
- ❏ Try out a new recipe
- ❏ Watch a movie

Make your own self-care checklist and hang it where you can see it!

"It will be harder to take care of others if you are not taking care of yourself. Schedule time for yourself and keep the appointment just as you would if it were a business meeting." Jessica Setnick, RD, LD CEDRD

Step 5: Manage your stress. Food and eating are often associated with times of stress and emotions. Food feels good and can often offer comfort and satisfaction in times of stress. No matter how much we try to balance our days and eat healthy meals and snacks, stress or upsetting situations can get the best of us. In fact, when Oliver and Wardle observed the effects of stress on eating behaviors of students, they calculated a 73% increase in snacking among those students with high stress levels.

Whatever the emotion you may be feeling, journaling is an excellent way to become aware of the current situation and organize your thoughts. There are various types of journaling you can do to manage stress. Take the time to try out each type of journal and see what works for you.

Trash Journal
Get messy! Using a simple notebook or a stack of scrap paper, write out all the confusing, overwhelming thoughts you have in your head and simply detach from them. Having them on paper can help you stop avoiding them and address them once and for all. There is no need to reread your entries or share them with anyone. This can be done in the morning to start your day with a clear mind, or in the evening to ease yourself to sleep.

Success journal

Keep track of the daily successes big and small. This should be celebrated for it is a combination of these small steps that make up the journey you are on. When we focus just on the weight we minimize all of the healthy behaviors we have practiced and feel like giving up when in reality SO much has changed and there is so much to be proud of.

Positivity Journal

Write down the negative thoughts in your head and come up with ways to respond to them in a neutral or positive fashion. Turn the negative monologue into a dialogue.

Inspirational
Journal
Keep a journal of
inspirational
quotes and
images that you
can flip through
as needed.

Gratitude
Journal
Take time at the
end of each day
to write what
you are thankful
for. Remembering
these things can
help you see the
big picture during
times of sadness
and stress.

Try one of these journaling methods tonight. What did you think?

_____

_____

_____

_____

_____

Step 6: Improve your sleep hygiene. Not only is a good night's sleep crucial for a healthy body and mind, recent research reveals that inadequate sleep may lead to increased risk of health problems. Complications from inadequate sleep (less than five hours a night) include:

- Decreased metabolism
- Increased fat storage
- Increased long term risk for heart diseases (high blood pressure, stroke, heart attack), diabetes (and other metabolic problems), mood disorders, and cognitive deterioration (poor memory, slowed thinking)
- Disruption of hormones responsible for decreasing eating satisfaction (leptin) and stimulating your appetite (ghrelin)
- Increased frequency of eating and increased food intake by approximately 300 calories

Tips for Achieving Better Sleep

- **Avoid caffeine, nicotine, and alcohol.** Caffeine stays in your system for about six hours, so keep that in mind if you're grabbing the early evening coffee.
- **Move your body regularly.** For some, movement close to bed helps with better sleep while some feel more awake after movement. Experiment and see what works best for you.
- **Create a bedtime ritual.** Regular, soothing habits will clue your body into relaxation (reading, taking a bath, and/or sipping warm milk).
- **Manage your sleep environment.** Make your room as comfortable, dark, and pleasant as possible. Invest in black-out shades or a light-canceling face mask. Consider using a white noise machine and/or earplugs if your home or neighborhood is noisy.
- **Only use your bedroom for rest and relaxation.** Do not use your bed for activities such as business, eating, or homework.
- **Keep regular sleep times, even on the weekends.** Try not to exceed a two hour difference from day to day.
- **Get exposure to sunlight.** Try for at least 30 minutes in the morning near a window and avoid bright lights in the evening including phones, tablets, computers, and TV screens.

Step 7. Incorporate joyful movement. Movement can help to connect mind and body, allowing you to feel comfortable in your own skin. As a REBEL we want you to think of movement in a new light. Instead of associating movement with losing weight and burning calories, focus on stress-relief, self-care, and health. Let's move away from the burden of "exercise," which implies something we HAVE to do to earn our food. Rest assured, this is not the case. We prefer to use the word movement which is good for your heart and soul. An example of exercise is walking on the treadmill which is good for your heart. But an example of movement is walking in nature, which is good for your heart and soul.

Take some time to answer these questions and explore how movement can best work for you.

1. Why is it important for you to incorporate joyful movement into your life?

_____

_____

_____

2. What were some of your favorite activities as a child or young adult?

  ❏ Dancing
  ❏ Skating
  ❏ Shooting hoops
  ❏ Jumping on a trampoline
  ❏ Playing games with others
  ❏ Bowling
  ❏ Hiking
  ❏ Playing tennis
  ❏ Other: _____

3. Do you prefer time to yourself or movement with a group?

  _____

  _____

4. Are you a morning person, or do you have more time at night?

  _____

  _____

5. How does your body, mind, and spirit feel after movement?

  _____

  _____

  _____

We truly believe that we find time for the things we value, and if movement is one of them (and it's ok if it's not yet) you will find time in your day to make it work. Often, lack of time is part of the default thinking that makes sense, but does not address the true reason you are not allowing movement to fit into your day. Perhaps you have some other concerns that we would like to address:

Do you have a fear of failing?
  REBEL Tip: Just as with dieting, it is hard to achieve a large, impractical, or unsustainable goal. As with food, movement doesn't have to be all or nothing. Choose types of movement that you enjoy, and there will be nothing to "fail."

Do you fear not being able to keep up?
  REBEL Tip: Start slowly and just take a walk around your house each day. You will build up your stamina, and then perhaps you can try joining up with others.

Are you afraid of injuries?
  REBEL Tip: Talk to your doctor about the best forms of movement for you, and work with a professional who can show you the correct way to do a certain movement.

Have you felt humiliated doing activities in the past?

REBEL Tip: Remember you deserve to own whatever space you choose to do your movement in whether that is at a gym, in a class, or in a pool. If it's too much to handle at once, try movement on your own while listening to music or a book on tape. Or, pair up with a supportive friend before joining a larger class.

Step 8: Radically love your body. Isn't it sad that loving your body is such a radical idea? We live in a world where hating your body is normalized. As REBELs, it's essential to go against the grain and learn how to radically love your body. This process takes time, but we will give you some tools you can use to start on this path. To begin, it will be important to explore your body image as it stands now so you can understand it better. It's not just what you see in the mirror but also how you feel.

"Body image refers to an individual's perception, feelings, and attitudes toward his or her own body, or how he or she experiences the body psychologically."
Carolyn Costin, M.A., M.Ed., MFT, *Your Dieting Daughter*

Take some time to answer the following questions:

1. Do you ever remember a time when you were not concerned with your weight, body shape, or size? What do you remember about that time? What was different? What changed?

     _____
     _____
     _____

2. Aside from physical appearance, how would you describe a person who has positive body image? What do you think of him or her?

     _____
     _____
     _____

3. What things might you miss out on because of your opinion about your body?

     _____
     _____
     _____

4. If your seven year old niece, sister, daughter, or stranger came to you with negative thoughts on body image, shape, and size what would you say to them?

     _____
     _____
     _____

5. Can you remember any messages from the media, friends, family, or acquaintances that seemed to degrade your body image? How might you be able to limit the impact of these people?

_____

_____

_____

(Adapted from 8 Keys to Recovery from an Eating Disorder by Carolyn Costin and Gwen Schubert Grabb)

If you have spent a lifetime hating your body shape and size, loving your body may seem very foreign. However, the closer you get to respecting what your body has offered you in the past and what it continues to do for you on a daily basis, the more equipped you will be to care for that body, including giving it the nutrition it needs.

> Research shows that body movement can be a determining factor on how you feel. Have you heard people say "Fake it 'til you make it?" If you shy away and crouch down, you likely feel weak and helpless. On the other hand, if you stand tall and take up more space with your body, you will feel powerful and strong. Our non-verbal communication governs how we think and feel about ourselves. The more you can infuse positivity or even neutrality into your body, the closer you will get to ultimate acceptance.

"We're working hard to get women and men to change their relationship with their reflection, and each time they look in the mirror to say something positive about themselves—not necessarily about their appearance, but some affirmative statement about who they are in the world or what they have done well that day."
Cynthia M. Bulik, PhD, *Crave: Why You Binge Eat and How to Stop*

Step 9: Stop comparing. Many comparisons are natural and involuntary. We are taught in elementary school to compare a triangle to a rectangle, or the color red to the color blue. Activities like this typically don't have our minds forming opinions about whether red is better than blue, or if triangles are inferior to rectangles. We see—in our innocent, child-like lenses—that they are just *different*. There is no judgment or critical thoughts.

"Comparison is the thief of joy." Theodore Roosevelt

As we grow up and our filter becomes blotchy from what our friends say, what we read in magazines, and what we hear in the media, we often adopt a critical mentality. We naturally compare ourselves to others, but we often end up feeling like something is wrong with us, rather than just being able to end with the idea, *"Yes, we are different. If we weren't different, we wouldn't have our own identity."* Neither person is better than the other.

So how do you combat this comparison mentality? Well, instead of saying, *"Her legs are skinnier than mine,"* tell yourself, *"These legs allowed me to walk my child down the aisle."* Or rather than dwell on things like, *"I ate more than everyone at this dinner table,"* swing your thoughts to something more positive like, *"I ended up eating to a seven on the hunger scale, and I am satisfied."*

What are some aspects of your life or body that you have recently compared to another? How can you put your own REBEL spin on the comparison?

_____

_____

_____

"How would you feel if you were able to start practicing ACCEPTANCE of natural differences, rather than fighting it? Acceptance that the differences that are inevitable, are our own. We have to own them, embrace them. Catch yourself when you start down the critical, judgmental road of comparison."
Bobbi Boteler, RD, LD, CEDRD

Step 10: Squash "fat-shaming-talk." Self-talk is the inner voice that comforts us, infuriates us, makes us worry, and encourages us. For some, this self-talk turns into fat-shaming-talk or body bashing, and these thoughts fuel feelings of negative body shape and size. This can lead to sabotaging behaviors like skipping meals and under eating. For some, these bullying thoughts are like a radio with the volume on full blast that is turned on all day. Many times this voice feeds the thought that you are "fat," that the food you are eating is "bad," and that your weight makes you "undesirable." Fat-shaming-talk drags you down along with those around you.

How can you REBELLIOUSLY break free of this criticism? If others around you are taking part in fat-shaming-talk, point it out. If you need to, remove yourself from a toxic situation and surround yourself with those who do not take part in fat-shaming-talk.

"In a survey that a colleague and I reported in 2011 in the *Psychology of Women Quarterly*, we found that more than 90 percent of college women reported engaging in fat-shaming-talk — despite the fact that only 9 percent were actually overweight." Renee Elgeln

Talk to yourself as you would your best friend. If you realize a negative thought pops into your head, be kind to yourself. Although it may feel unnatural at first, focus on all the positive things that your body can do, and start learning to accept and ultimately love the body you have now.

Part of being a REBEL is practicing *positive* affirmations and behaviors. Here are some positive affirmations we love to use:

- *I am thankful for my body because it allows me to run, hike, and walk, and it carries me to all the places I want to go.*
- *I want to be a role model for other girls and women by accepting my body.*
- *What good is having this body if I don't have any fun in it?*
- *My body is a trusted and treasured home for me to enjoy and use fully rather than as an aesthetic object.*
- *I will look at myself as a whole person rather than choosing to focus on specific body parts.*
- *I will wear clothes that are comfortable and make me feel good about my body.*
- *I will appreciate all that my body can do.*

Do any of these positive affirmations resonate with you? Can you think of others that might work for you? Repeat these each day to become familiar with these positive statements.

_____

_____

_____

"If a person wants to change their body…they have to have self-compassion to take care of themselves first by focusing on sustainable and realistic lifestyle habits that feel good to them."
Leslie Schilling, MA, RD, CSSD and Rebecca Scritchfield, MA, RD, ACSM-HFS, creators of RDs for Body Confidence,
http://www.rd4bc.com

Putting It into Practice: Get Your Hands Dirty

Let's face it, we live in a world where the dieting mindset is ingrained in our culture. To stay out of the dieting prison, you have to be persistent and continue to empower yourself each and every day.

You now have the street smarts to determine **what** to eat, **when** to eat, **where** to eat, **why** you are eating, and **how** to nourish your mind, body, and soul. Now it's time to get your hands dirty and actually practice being a REBEL. Let's move on to the final chapter and put all these skills in place so you can learn to live joyfully and never go back to the dieting prison.

"Be Bold. Be Brave. Be a REBEL!" REBEL Dietitians®

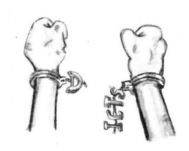

CHAPTER 5: Live Joyfully

Breaking the Shackles

Here are our REBEL confessions to the food police and diet industry:

- *We go out to dinner and enjoy our favorite food, macaroni and cheese.*
- *We eat ice cream with our kids (and use our favorite toppings).*
- *We have put an end to fat-shaming-talk in conversations with our friends and our family.*
- *We cook with real butter.*
- *We love pasta, pizza, and potatoes and fit them into our meals.*
- *We don't log calories, and we avoid diet paraphernalia.*
- *We legalize all food.*
- *We prioritize exquisite self-care.*
- *Diets no longer have a hold over what we eat and how we feel about our bodies.*

Spreading the REBELLION

Now that you have broken from the shackles of your dieting prison, you have the ability to spread the sweet REBELLION and help keep other people out of this prison. You can empower your loved ones to nourish and accept themselves and never diet again.

Raising REBELS

Children whose parents have been "incarcerated" in dieting prison are more likely to follow in their footsteps. Almost half of American children between first and third grades want to be thinner, and half of nine and ten year old girls are dieting. In one study, approximately two-thirds of girls reported that their mother dieted or talked about her own weight, and nearly half of the girls reported that their mother encouraged them to diet. You have the power to break the cycle!

In order to help their children, parents often start putting them on diets, pressuring the children to eat certain foods while limiting others. Unfortunately, these good intentions often lead to overeating, selective eating, and children sneaking these forbidden foods.

Empower your children to make their own healthy decisions about food. Children are wiser than we often give them credit for. As they grow up and go to friends' houses, start driving, go to college, or move out on their own, they will have unlimited access to whatever foods they want. It is important to help them make the decisions about food now, so they can be confident in food choices as adults. It is the parents' job to model healthy behaviors such as eating regularly throughout the day, eating a variety of foods—including everything from vegetables to dessert—and recognizing and accepting their hunger and fullness cues.

If you are concerned about your child's weight, it is best to improve the whole family's eating habits and leave weight out of the discussion. Your children may not talk about it, but they witness your relationship with food, as well as your feelings about food and your body. These observations frame their own future relationship with food.

What are some good messages for our children? Well, we know that fine tuning nutrition behaviors and physical activity can result in health improvements such as lower blood glucose, blood lipids, and cholesterol with little or no weight loss. Also, children with positive self-images are more likely to eat well and have healthy lifestyles regardless of their weight. The bottom line is to help children accept and value themselves and others regardless of differences in body shape and size.

Friends, Family, and Acquaintances

POST CARD

PLACE STAMP HERE

Dieting Dave,
It's not the destination; it's the journey. For years I focused my time and energy on the destination of being thinner, of weighing what I imagined to be my "perfect weight," and of fitting back into my favorite jeans from high school. I was skeptical to leave that world behind. After all, that is all I knew. But, I finally understood how this cycle was going to follow me forever. I picked up the REBEL Against Dieting Workbook and began freeing myself from the dieting prison step by step. The journey was not a piece of cake, but I did learn to allow myself a piece of cake and SAVOR it. I am still tempted by the allure of dieting, but I now KNOW that a life with dieting is a life away from what I value most. By REBELing, I learned that I can trust my body again, eat the foods I enjoy, and spend my time on ME, not stressing about food! You can too. Do it sooner rather than later! Get your life back!
~FREE from Dieting Darla

Dieting Dave
Diet Prison

In hindsight, you may finally be able to recognize that you were in dieting prison. Now it may be clear from the outside that some of your friends, family, or acquaintances may be trapped. You can be a positive force and a REBEL role model by introducing them to the REBEL way of life if they are open and curious.

But, sometimes people are not yet ready to break out of the diet prison. Even though everyone won't be ready to join the REBELLION, you must stay positive. Refute fat-shaming-talk comments, let dieting crazes roll off your back, and continue living according to your REBEL values.

REBEL Pledge

The offense was dieting, and it could have continued its cycle throughout your life, keeping you incarcerated. You gave up your individuality, trust in your body, and your decision making capabilities. BUT, you made a choice to ditch the diet, and you are out on parole. These are the guidelines of your parole that can help you stay out of prison:

> **R** = RESIST Diets
> **E** = EAT Like a REBEL
> **B** = BUILD Confidence in Your Eating
> **E** = EMPOWER Yourself
> **L** = LIVE Joyfully

Now that you are out on parole, it is time to take the final oath:

REBEL Toolbox

REBEL Resources We Love

While preparing this workbook for our readers, we consulted a variety of wonderful resources. We encourage you to deepen your knowledge of REBEL eating concepts by exploring the books and videos on this list.

8 Keys to Recovery from an Eating Disorder by Effective Strategies from Therapeutic Practice and Personal Experience by Carolyn Costin, Gwen Schubert Grabb, foreword by Babette Rothschild

50 Ways to Soothe Yourself Without Food by Susan Albers, PSY.D

Anatomy of the Soul by Curt Thompson, MD

The Anorexia Workbook by Michelle Heffner, MA and Georg H. Eifert, PhD

Beyond a Shadow of a Diet, second edition by Judith Matz, LCSW and Ellen Frankel, LCSW

The Big Book of ACT Metaphors by Jill A. Stoddard, PhD and Niloofar Afari, PhD

The Binge Eating and Compulsive Overeating Workbook: An Integrated Approach to Overcoming Disordered Eating by Carolyn Coker Ross MD, MPH

Binge No More: Your Guide to Overcoming Disordered Eating by Joyce D. Nash, PhD

The Body Image Workbook: An Eight Step Program for Learning to Like Your Looks by Thomas F. Cash, PhD

Body Respect by Linda Bacon and Lucy Aphramor, PhD, RD

But I Deserve Chocolate! The 50 Most Common Diet-Derailing Excuses and How to Outwit Them by Susan Albers, PsyD

Crave: Why You Binge Eat and How to Stop by Cynthia M. Bulik

Desperately Seeking Self: An Inner Guidebook for People with Eating Problems by Viola Fodor

The Dialectical Behavior Therapy Skills Workbook by Matthew McKay, PhD, Jeffrey Wood, PsyD and Jeffrey Brantley, MD

Eat What You Love, Love What You Eat for Binge Eating by Michelle May and Kari Anderson

Eat What You Love, Love What You Eat by Michelle May, MD

Eat What You Love, Love What You Eat, With Diabetes by Michelle May, MD

Eat, Drink, and Be Mindful by Susan Albers, PsyD

Eating Mindfully, Second Edition by Susan Albers, PsyD

The Emotional Eater's Repair Manual by Julie M. Simon

End Emotional Eating by Jennifer L Taitz, PsyD

Ending Overeating by Ken Goss, DClinPsy

The Diet Survivor's Handbook: 60 Lessons in Eating, Acceptance and Self Care by Judith Matz, LCSW and Ellen Frankel, LCSW

The Food and Feeling Workbook: A Full Course Meal on Emotional Health by Karen R. Koenig, LCSW, MEd

The Food and Feelings Workbook by A Full Course Meal on Emotional Health by Karen R. Koenig, LCSW, M.Ed

The Happiness Trap: How to Stop Struggling and Start Living by Russ Harris foreword by Steven Hayes, PhD

Having Your All: How Self Care Leads to an Energized, Empowered and Effective Life by Emma Fogt, MBA, MS, RDN and Nisha Shah, MPH, RDN

Healing Your Hungry Heart by Joanna Poppink

Health at Every Size by Linda Bacon, PhD

Intuitive Eating: Make Peace with Food, Mind and Body by Evelyn Tribole, MS, RD (https://www.youtube.com/watch?v=eSpzf72S6IY)

Mindful Eating: A Guide to Rediscovering a Healthy and Joyful Relationship with Food by Jan Chozen Bays, MD

Nutrition Counseling in the Treatment of Eating Disorders by Marcia Herrin and Maria Larkin

Outsmarting Overeating by Karen R. Koenig

Overcoming Overeating How to Break the Diet/Binge Cycle and Live a Healthier More Satisfying Life by Jane Hirschmann and Carol Munter

The Overworked Person's Guide to Better Nutrition by Jill Weisenberger

Picture Cook: See. Make. Eat by Katie Shelly

Real Moms Love to Eat by Beth Aldrich

The Relaxation and Stress Reduction Workbook by Martha Davis, PhD, Elizabeth Robbins Eshelman, MSW and Matthew McKay, PhD

The Rules of "Normal" Eating: A Commonsense Approach for Dieters, Overeaters, Undereaters, Emotional Eaters, and Everyone In Between! by Karen R. Koenig, LICSW, M.Ed

Treatment Plans and Interventions for Bulimia and Binge Eating Disorder by Rene D. Zweig and Robert L. Leahy

Why Weight? A Guide to Ending Compulsive Eating by Geneen Roth

The Woman's Comfort Book: A Self Nurturing Guide for Restoring Balance in your Life by Jennifer Louden

Women Food and God: An Unexpected Path to Almost Everything by Geneen Roth

Your Dieting Daughter by Carolyn Costin

Spectracell Nutrient Functions Chart

http://www.spectracell.com/media/uploaded/d/0e2008085_document-303-nutrient-chart.pdf

Nutrient	Function	Where It is Found
Vitamin E	Antioxidant, regulates oxidation reactions, stabilizes cell membrane, immune function, protects against cardiovascular disease, cataracts, macular degeneration	Wheat germ, liver, eggs, nuts, seeds, cold-pressed vegetable oils, dark leafy greens, sweet potatoes, avocados, asparagus
Calcium	Bones, teeth, helps heart, nerves, muscles, helps body systems work properly, needs other nutrients to function	Dairy, wheat/soy flour, molasses, Brazil nuts, broccoli, cabbage, dark leafy greens, hazelnuts, oysters, sardines, canned salmon
Chromium	Assists insulin function, increases fertility, carbohydrate/fat metabolism, essential for fetal growth/ development	Supplementation, brewer's yeast, whole grains, seafood, green beans, broccoli, prunes, nuts, potatoes, meat
Magnesium	300 biochemical reactions, muscle/nerve function, heart rhythm, immune system, strong bones, regulates calcium, copper, zinc, potassium, Vitamin D	Green vegetables, beans, peas, nuts, seeds, whole unprocessed grains
Selenium	Antioxidant, works with vitamin E, immune function, prostaglandin production	Brewer's yeast, wheat germ, liver, butter, cold water fish, shellfish, garlic, whole grains, sunflower seeds, Brazil nuts
Zinc	Supports enzymes, immune system, wound healing, taste/smell, DNA synthesis, normal growth and development during pregnancy, childhood, and adolescence	Oysters, red meat, poultry, tempeh (fermented soybeans), wheat, asparagus, avocados, peanut butter
Copper	Bone formation, involved in healing process, energy production, hair and skin coloring, taste sensitivity, stimulates iron absorption, helps metabolize several fatty acids	Oysters, seeds, dark leafy vegetables, organ meats, dried legumes, whole grain breads, nuts, shellfish, chocolate, soybeans, oats, blackstrap molasses
Vitamin B1	Carbohydrate conversion, breaks down fats and protein, digestion, nervous system, skin, hair, eyes, mouth, liver, immune system	Pork, whole grain and enriched cereals, brown rice, wheat germ, bran, brewer's yeast, blackstrap molasses
Vitamin B2	Metabolism, carbohydrate conversion, breaks down fats and protein, digestion, nervous system, skin, hair, eyes, mouth, liver	Brewer's yeast, almonds, whole grains, wheat germ, mushrooms, soy, dairy, eggs, green vegetables
Vitamin B3	Energy, digestion, nervous system, skin, hair, eyes, liver, eliminates toxins, sex and stress-related hormones, improves circulation	Beets, brewer's yeast, meat, poultry, organ meats, fish, seeds, nuts

97

Vitamin B6	Enzyme, protein metabolism, red blood cell production, reduces homocysteine, nerve and muscle cells, DNA/RNA, B12 absorption, immune function	Poultry, tuna, salmon, shrimp, beef liver, lentils, soybeans, seeds, nuts, avocados, bananas, carrots, brown rice, bran, wheat germ, whole grain flour
Vitamin B12	Healthy nerve cells, DNA/RNA, red blood cell production, iron function	Fish, meat, poultry, eggs milk, milk products
Biotin	Carbohydrate, fat, amino acid metabolism	Salmon, meats, vegetables, grains, legumes, lentils, egg yolks, milk, sweet potatoes, seeds, nuts, wheat germ
Folate	Mental health, infant DNA/RNA, adolescence and pregnancy, works with B12 to regulate red blood cell production, iron function, lower homocysteine	Supplementation, fortified grains, tomato juice, green vegetables, black eyed-peas, lentils, beans
Pantothenate	Red blood cell production, sex and stress-related hormones, immune function, healthy digestion, helps use other vitamins	Meat, vegetables, whole grains, legumes, lentils, egg yolks, milk, sweet potatoes, seeds, nuts, wheat germ, salmon
Vitamin A	Eyes, immune function, skin, essential cell growth and development	Milk, eggs, liver, fortified cereals, orange or green vegetables, fruits
Vitamin C	Enzyme activation, second messenger roles (transmitting hormonal information), blood clotting, cell and cell organelle membrane function, nerve impulse transmission and muscular contraction, tone and irritability	Supplementation, broccoli, Brussels sprouts, cantaloupe, cauliflower, citrus, guava, kiwi, papaya, parsley, peas, potatoes, peppers, parsley, rose hips, strawberries, tomatoes
Vitamin D	Calcium and phosphorus levels, calcium absorption, bone mineralization	Sunlight, milk, egg yolks, liver, fish
Vitamin K	Aids in the formation of clotting factors and bone proteins and the formation of glucose into glycogen for storage in the liver	Kale, green tea, turnip greens, spinach, broccoli, lettuce, cabbage, beef liver, asparagus, watercress, cheese, oats, peas, whole wheat

REBELLIOUS Recipes

Breakfast

Basic Scrambled Eggs (for one)
Ingredients
- 2 eggs
- 2 T. milk
- ¼ c. shredded cheese
- Garlic, oregano, and pepper (to flavor)
- Olive oil or cooking spray

Crack the eggs in a bowl and add milk and cheese. Mix with a fork or a whisk until smooth. Add the spices to desired flavor (about ½ teaspoon each)

Heat the sauté pan on stove with cooking spray or about ½ tablespoon of olive oil. Pour the eggs on the heated pan; stir the eggs occasionally. Cook until the eggs are no longer runny.

Sunny Side Up Eggs
Ingredients
- 1 egg
- Cooking spray or olive oil
- 1–2 T. of water
- Oregano and pepper

Spray a sauté pan with cooking spray or coat with olive oil. Heat the pan over medium heat and crack the egg into it; season with oregano and pepper while the egg is cooking. Once the edges of the egg are white and no longer clear, add the water to the pan. Cover the pan as the water is sizzling and let the egg cook for about 30 seconds. The water will steam the pan and cook the top of the egg! You will have an awesome looking sunny side up egg in minutes.

Hard Boiled Eggs
Ingredients
- Eggs (one or two per person)
- Water

Fill large pot with water and place the eggs in the pot. Turn up the heat, cover the pot, and cook the eggs for 13 minutes. Once eggs are finished, rinse with cold water.

REBEL Tip: Add hard boiled eggs to a Greek or Caesar salad for extra protein.

Eggs in a Mug
Ingredients
- 2 eggs
- 2 T. of milk
- Pepper, oregano, garlic, and salt for seasoning
- 2 T. of shredded cheddar cheese
- 1 whole English muffin
- ½ c. fresh spinach
- 2 tomato slices
- 2 T. hummus (optional)

Mix the eggs, milk, and cheese; put the mixture in a mug. Cook in the microwave for 45 seconds. Take the mug out and stir. Cook in the microwave for another 35 to 40 seconds until slightly firm. While the eggs are cooking, toast the English muffin. When the eggs and English muffin are done, spread the hummus on the English muffin. Put the eggs on the muffin and top with the spinach and tomato.

Sausage Frittata with Mushrooms
Ingredients
- 1 T. olive oil
- 1 red onion, thinly sliced
- 1 link cooked andouille sausage, diced
- 8 oz. mushrooms (any variety)
- Salt and pepper
- 8 eggs
- ¼ c. crumbled goat cheese
- 12 chives or 3 scallions

Preheat oven to 375 ^{0}F. Heat in a large oven safe skillet or sauté pan over medium heat. When the pan is hot, add the oil and onion. Cook until translucent, about three minutes. Add the andouille sausage and mushroom and continue to sauté, about five minutes. Season with salt and pepper. Beat the eggs vigorously with a fork or a whisk, then add to the skillet, along with the goat cheese and chives or scallions, if using.

Place in oven and bake until the eggs have set, about 20 minutes. Let cool, slice into four portions, and top with more chives if you like.

REBEL Tip: This is a quick recipe to make any day of the week. Prepare everything the night before, and all you have to do is cook the frittata the next morning. Serve with toast and fruit. You can customize the recipe, substituting the mushrooms, sausage, and goat cheese for any of these combinations:

- 8 spears of cooked, chopped asparagus, and 2 oz. chopped smoked salmon
- ¼ c. sun dried tomatoes, ¼ c. chopped olives, and ½ c. crumbled feta
- 1 c. sautéed spinach, 4 strips of bacon, and ½ c. grated gruyere cheese
- 1 c. sautéed zucchini, 1 c. ricotta, and 8 to 10 chopped mint leaves

Muffin Tin Eggs (12 servings)
Ingredients
- 2 T. of olive oil
- 6 eggs
- ¾ c. frozen spinach (defrosted and patted dry with paper towel) or chopped fresh spinach
- ½ c. frozen mixed peppers (defrosted) or chopped fresh red bell pepper
- ½ c. shredded cheese
- Pepper and salt to flavor

Preheat oven to 350 °F. Mix all ingredients in bowl. Evenly distribute the mixture in muffin tins. Bake for 10 to 12 minutes. Eat with whole wheat and butter!

REBEL Tip: Double the recipe and freeze half for later!

Huevos Rancheros (4 servings)
Ingredients
- 1 – 16 oz. can whole, peeled, low-sodium tomatoes with juice
- ½ small onion, chopped
- 1 clove garlic, chopped (may substitute dash garlic powder)
- 1 T. chopped jalapeño pepper
- ¼ c. chopped cilantro
- Juice of one lime (or 2 T. lime juice)
- Salt and pepper to taste
- 1 can of black beans
- Pinch of ground cumin
- 8 eggs
- 8 corn tortillas

Combine the tomatoes, onion, garlic, chipotle, cilantro, and half of the lime juice in the food processor. Pulse until well blended but still slightly chunky. Season with salt and pepper. Mix the black beans, cumin, and remaining lime juice in a bowl. Season with salt and pepper. Use the back of a fork and lightly mash up the beans, adding a splash of warm water if necessary.

Coat a large, nonstick skillet or sauté pan with nonstick cooking spray and heat over medium heat. Break the eggs into the skillet, cook until the whites have set but the yolks are still loose and runny. On a separate burner, heat a medium skillet over medium heat and add the tortillas, two at a time, cooking for one minute on each side until lightly toasted.

To assemble dish, spread the tortillas with the beans, top with eggs, and top the eggs with the salsa. Garnish with more cilantro if you like and serve immediately.

Sweet Potato and Spinach Egg Scramble (4 servings)
Ingredients

- 8 eggs
- ⅓ c. milk
- ½ t. ground cumin
- ¼ t. salt
- ¼ t. ground black pepper
- 1 T. butter
- 2 medium sweet potatoes (about 1 pound total), peeled, quartered lengthwise, thinly sliced
- 1 green onion, sliced
- 2 c. baby spinach
- Fresh Italian (flat-leaf) parsley
- Bottled hot pepper sauce (optional)

In a medium bowl, whisk together eggs, milk, cumin, salt, and pepper; set aside. In a large skillet, melt butter over medium heat. Add sweet potato and green onion. Cook, stirring occasionally, until potatoes are lightly browned and just tender, about eight minutes. Add spinach. Cook until slightly wilted, about one minute.

Pour egg mixture over potato mixture in skillet. Cook, without stirring, until mixture begins to set on bottom and around edges. Lift and fold partially cooked egg mixture so the uncooked portion flows underneath. Continue cooking for two to three minutes or until egg mixture is cooked through but still glossy and moist. Sprinkle with fresh parsley. Remove from heat and serve at once. Season with bottled hot pepper sauce.

Quiche with Feta, Salmon, and Dill
Ingredients
- Pie crust dough, rolled out (store bought or homemade)
- One 9-inch x 2-inch high tart pan with removable bottom (may use a 10-inch pie pan)
- 1 T. olive oil
- 4 medium shallots, thinly sliced (about ½ c.)
- 6 oz. smoked salmon, chopped
- 4 oz. feta cheese, crumbled
- 6 large eggs
- 2 c. milk
- 1 c. cream
- 2 T. chopped fresh dill
- 1 t. lemon zest
- 2 ½ t. salt
- Dash of freshly ground black pepper

Preheat oven to 375 ^{0}F. Place pie crust in tart pan or in pie plate. Heat oil in a small skillet on medium heat. Add the shallots and cook until translucent (a couple minutes). Remove from heat. Whisk eggs in a medium bowl. Whisk in feta cheese. Whisk in milk, cream, dill, lemon zest, and black pepper. Whisk in the shallots.

Line bottom of the quiche crust with half of the smoked salmon. Pour half of the egg mixture over the salmon in the quiche shell. Layer the remaining salmon and pour the remaining egg mixture over it.

Place the quiche pan on a foil-lined rimmed baking sheet. Transfer to oven. Bake at 375 ^{0}F for 15 minutes. Lower the heat to 350 ^{0}F and bake until just set in the center, about 30 to 40 minutes. Remove from oven and cool on a wire rack for 15 minutes before serving.

REBEL Tip: Serve with a garden salad for a complete meal. This would also make a delicious addition to any brunch.

Omelet with Spinach, Onions, and Goat Cheese
Ingredients

- 2 eggs
- Handful of spinach
- ¼ c. chopped onions
- 1 oz. goat cheese
- ½ t. oil
- Cooking spray
- Salt and pepper to taste

Crack the eggs in a bowl. Whisk slightly and season with salt and pepper. Heat a small, nonstick skillet on the stove over medium high heat. Add ½ teaspoon of oil and sauté the onions. Once the onions are soft and translucent, add spinach until wilted. Remove from pan. In that same pan, reduce the heat to low, spray with cooking spray, and pour in the egg mixture. Once the eggs are almost set, add the onion and spinach mixture to half of the omelet. Crumble the goat cheese on top of the spinach mixture. Let it melt for a few minutes, then fold the omelet in half, covering the spinach and cheese mixture.

REBEL Tip: This omelet recipe is very versatile. You can use any kind of vegetables or cheese that you like!

Salmon and Cream Cheese Breakfast
Ingredients

- 1 slice of whole grain bread, toasted
- 4 oz. smoked salmon
- 2 T. of cream cheese (chive cream cheese would taste great!)

Spread the cream cheese on the toast, top with smoked salmon. Enjoy!

Avocado and Cheese Breakfast Toast
Ingredients

- 1 slice of whole grain bread, toasted
- 2 slices of cheese
- ½ avocado cut in slices

Put the cheese on the toasted bread and toast in a toaster oven for an additional minute. Spread avocado slices on the cheese. Enjoy!

Peanut Butter and Banana Breakfast Toast
Ingredients
- 1 slice of whole grain bread, toasted
- 2 T. peanut butter
- 1 banana
- Honey and cinnamon for flavor and sweetness (optional)

Spread peanut butter on the toast. Slice bananas and layer them on top. Top it all off with honey and cinnamon!

Refried Beans and Cheese Breakfast Toast
Ingredients
- 1 slice of whole grain bread, toasted
- ¼ c. refried beans
- 1 slice of cheese
- 2 T. salsa

Spread refried beans on the toast, add salsa; top with cheese. Toast for another minute in toaster oven.

REBEL Tip: Make this into an egg sandwich by adding some vegetables (like lettuce and tomato), a sunny side up egg, and another piece of toasted bread! For more breakfast toast ideas see the infographic in Chapter 2, page 41.

Yogurt Parfait
Ingredients
- 1 c. of Greek yogurt
- ¾ c. of fruit (either fresh or frozen)
- Toppings, your choice: ¼ c. slivered almonds, 1 T. chia seeds, 1 T. flax seeds, ¼ c. of granola, 2 T. of honey roasted peanuts, ¼ c. walnuts, ¼ c. dry cereal

Layer Greek yogurt in a bowl. Add your favorite fruit. Sprinkle on extra toppings of your choice.

REBEL Tip: You can make the parfait the night before and leave it in the fridge for a grab-and-go breakfast. (If using granola or dry cereal, do not put it on top the day before, or it will get soggy. Put in a separate container to add right before eating). For more yogurt parfait ideas, see the infographic in Chapter 2, page 42.

Klara's Homemade Granola
Ingredients
- 3 c. of rolled oats
- 1 c. almonds
- ½ c. honey
- ¼ c. canola oil
- ¾ t. of regular salt

Add-ins (optional):
- 1–2 c. of seeds (sunflower, pumpkin, etc.)
- 1 c. coconut (large unsweetened flakes)
- 1 c. dried fruit—add after baking
- 1 t. spices (cinnamon, cardamom, nutmeg, ginger)
- ¼ c. cocoa (add before baking) or 1 c. chocolate chips (add after baking)
- 1 egg white (reduce oil by 2–4 T.)

Measure oats, almonds, seeds, salt, and spices into a large bowl. (If using cocoa or coconut, add now.) Add honey, oil, and egg white (if using) and stir together.

Bake on a baking sheet at 300 °F for 30 to 45 minutes, stirring after about 20 minutes. Stop when granola is lightly browned and toasted. Let the granola cool completely in the pan, stir in the fruit, (and if you are using them, the chocolate chips), then store in an airtight container.

Overnight Oats
Ingredients
- ½ c. quick oats
- ½ c. Greek yogurt (plain or flavored)
- ½ c. milk of choice
- Dash of cinnamon
- Honey to flavor

Put all ingredients together and mix. Put in fridge to store overnight.

REBEL Tip: Mix up overnight oats by adding in your favorite fruits.
- Banana nut: Add in banana slices and peanuts
- Berry Nice: Add in blueberries, raspberries and/or strawberry slices
- Flavored yogurt: Use various flavors of Greek yogurt like key lime, pomegranate, black raspberry, vanilla, etc. to add an extra burst of taste to the overnight oats

Alex's Old Fashioned Oatmeal
Ingredients
- ½ c. old fashioned or quick oats
- ½ c. water
- ½ c. milk of choice
- ½ banana, cut in slices
- 2 T. raisins or dried cranberries
- 1 T. crunchy peanut butter
- Honey and cinnamon for flavor
- 1 T. flax seed

Add oats, milk, and water in a microwaveable safe bowl. Microwave according to the directions on the box. Mix in banana slices, peanut butter, raisins (or dried cranberries), honey, cinnamon, and flax seed.

REBEL Tip: Make this the night before and store in the fridge, can be eaten cold or reheated.

Pumpkin Spice Oatmeal
Ingredients
- 1/2 c. dry, unflavored oats
- 3 T. pumpkin puree
- Sprinkle of cinnamon, nutmeg, and vanilla (can substitute pumpkin spice flavor)
- 2 t. brown sugar
- Splash of milk or water to cook

Mix everything together in a microwave safe bowl, and microwave for one minute.

REBEL Tip: For more oatmeal combination ideas, see the infographic in Chapter 2, page 42.

REBEL Cheesecake Smoothie
Ingredients
- ½ c. cottage cheese
- 1 banana, cut into slices
- 1 c. milk
- 1 t. vanilla extract
- 1 t. cinnamon

Put all ingredients in the blender. Blend on high for about one minute. Check the consistency of the smoothie. Continue to blend until smooth.

Strawberry Banana Smoothie
Ingredients

- ½ c. silken tofu
- 1 banana, cut into slices
- 1 c. of orange juice
- ¾ c. strawberries (fresh or frozen; if fresh, cut into slices)
- 1 c. crushed iced

Put all ingredients in the blender. Blend on high for about one minute. Check the consistency of the smoothie. Continue to blend until smooth.

Chocolate Nut Butter Smoothie
Ingredients

- 1 c. chocolate milk
- 1 banana, cut into slices
- 2 T. nut butter (any kind will do—almond butter, peanut butter, cashew butter, etc.)
- 1 T. cocoa powder

Put all ingredients in the blender. Blend on high for about one minute. Check the consistency of the smoothie. Continue to blend until smooth.

Blueberry Vanilla Smoothie
Ingredients

- ½ c. plain Greek yogurt
- 1 c. milk
- 1 c. blueberries (fresh or frozen)
- 2 T. ground flax seeds (optional)
- 1 t. vanilla

Put all ingredients in the blender. Blend on high for about one minute. Check the consistency of the smoothie. Continue to blend until smooth.

REBEL Tip: For more smoothie ideas, refer to the smoothie infographic in Chapter 2, page 43

Lunch

Peanut Butter and Jelly Pinwheel Wraps
Ingredients
- 1 – 10" wrap
- 2 T. peanut butter
- 1 T. jelly, any flavor

Spread the peanut butter and jelly on the wrap. Roll up the wrap. Cut horizontally into six smaller pinwheel wraps.

Cream Cheese and Cucumber Pinwheel Wraps
Ingredients
- 1 – 10" wrap
- 2 T. cream cheese
- 1 cucumber, sliced
- Pepper to flavor

Spread the cream cheese on the wrap and add the cucumber slices. Roll up the wrap. Cut horizontally into six smaller pinwheel wraps.

Turkey and Cheese Pinwheel Wraps
Ingredients
- 1 – 10" wrap
- 3–4 slices of deli meat turkey
- 1–2 slices of your favorite cheese
- Lettuce, tomato, and onions as toppings
- Mustard (optional)

Lay the turkey and cheese on the wrap. Add the lettuce, tomatoes, and onions. Roll up the wrap. Cut horizontally into six smaller pinwheel wraps.

Hummus and Vegetables Pinwheel Wrap
Ingredients
- 1 – 10" wrap
- ¼ c. hummus
- 4 oz. cooked chicken, sliced
- Avocado slices
- ¼ c. shredded cheese of choice
- Vegetable add-ons: spinach, tomatoes, onions, mushrooms, shredded carrots

Spread hummus on wrap. Layer chicken, avocado, cheese, and your choice of vegetables. Roll up the wrap. Cut horizontally into 6 smaller pinwheel wraps.

Cold Vegetable Pizza *(prepare the night before)*
Ingredients
- 1 pita bread
- ¼–½ c. marinara sauce
- ¼–½ c. shredded mozzarella cheese
- ¼ c. turkey pepperoni (optional)
- 1 c. spinach (cooked, can be frozen)
- ½ onion chopped or sliced and separated
- ¼ t. garlic powder
- ¼ t. oregano
- Pepper, to taste
- 1 t. basil

Preheat oven or toaster oven to 350 °F. Place the pita bed on a piece of tin foil and season it with garlic, pepper, oregano, and basil. Spread the sauce on the pita and top with cheese and turkey pepperoni; add the spinach. Bake in oven for about five minutes.

REBEL Tip: If using frozen spinach, be sure to defrost the spinach first. You will then want to drain the spinach of excess liquid and blot between paper towels. If using fresh spinach, sauté on the stove for a few minutes until the leaves are cooked.

Black Bean and Turkey Chili
Ingredients
- 1 T. olive oil
- 1 yellow onion
- 4 cloves garlic
- ½ lb. ground turkey
- 3 – 15 oz. cans black beans
- 1 – 15 oz. can diced tomatoes with green chilies
- 3 oz. tomato paste (½ of a 6 oz. can or about ¼ c.)
- 1 T. chili powder
- ½ t. cumin
- ½ t. smoked paprika
- ½ t. oregano
- ¼ t. salt (or to taste)

Dice the onion and mince the garlic. Add the onion and garlic to a large pot with one tablespoon of olive oil and cook over medium-low heat just until softened (two to three minutes). Add the ground turkey to the pot and continue to sauté until the turkey is cooked through, about five to seven minutes. Break the turkey up into small crumbles with your spoon as it cooks.

Add the three cans of beans (un-drained), the diced tomatoes (un-drained), tomato paste, chili powder, cumin, smoked paprika, and oregano. Stir everything to combine.

Let the chili simmer for about 10 minutes to let the flavors blend and help the liquid thicken slightly. Taste the chili and add salt as needed—this will depend on the salt content of your canned goods. Serve with your favorite chili toppings.

REBEL Tip: Chop up some red, yellow, or green bell peppers and cook with the onions to add color and nutrition! Any kind of ground meat would work in this recipe. Change it up with chicken, lean ground beef, or sausage! You can also make this in the slow cooker! Begin by preparing the recipe as directed until the point where the meat is cooked through, and then pour hot mixture into a slow cooker. Add the rest of the ingredients to the slow cooker, and heat on low for six to eight hours or on high for four hours.

Pasta Salad with Vegetables and Chickpeas *(prepare the night before)*
Ingredients
- 2 c. dry penne pasta
- 2 – 15 oz. cans of chickpeas, drained
- 1 c. of sliced zucchini
- ¾ c. cherry tomatoes, sliced in half
- 2 T. of olive oil, divided
- Garlic powder

Cook pasta according to the directions on the box. While pasta is cooking, heat the garlic powder in one tablespoon olive oil in a pan. Once garlic is sizzling (about 30 seconds), add zucchini, and sauté for two to three minutes. Add tomatoes and sauté until both vegetables are soft.

Once the pasta is cooked, drain the water. Add the vegetables, chickpeas, and one tablespoon of olive oil to the pasta. Stir together. Add more garlic for flavoring. You can also add pepper, oregano, or red peppers for an extra kick. Refrigerate overnight for best flavor.

REBEL Tip: This recipe makes several servings, so you can pack it for lunch the whole week!

Avocado Tuna Salad
Ingredients
- ½ of ripe avocado
- 1 – 2.6 oz. packet or a 3 oz. can of tuna in water
- Salt and pepper

Optional Additions
- ½ c. red onion, chopped
- ½ c. chopped celery
- 1 hardboiled egg, chopped
- ¼ c. peeled and chopped pickles (variety, your choice)
- ½ c. peeled and chopped carrots
- 1 T. capers
- 2 T. mustard
- 2 T. olive oil

Drain the tuna and place in a bowl. Score the avocado with a paring knife, lengthwise and widthwise, and then scoop with spoon. Add to the bowl. Mash the avocado into the tuna with a fork until well blended. Stir in any additional ingredients that you wish. Add salt and pepper to taste.

REBEL Tip: The possibilities are endless with this tuna salad! Add on top of a mixed green salad, to two slices of whole grain bread, scoop with tortilla chips, or simply eat with a fork.

Honey Mustard Tuna Salad
Ingredients

- 1 packet of tuna or a 3 oz. can of tuna
- 1 T. of Greek yogurt (you can use mayonnaise if you prefer)
- 1 T. of honey mustard

Drain the tuna and put in a bowl. Mix in Greek yogurt and honey mustard. Use for tuna salad sandwich or over a bed of lettuce for a quick and easy lunch.

REBEL tip: If transporting to work, be sure to keep salad chilled, packing bread and toppings (lettuce, tomatoes, onion) separately. Make sandwich at the last minute.

Egg Salad Sandwich
Ingredients

- 1 hardboiled egg
- 1 T. Greek yogurt
- 2 T. avocado, mashed
- 1 T. chopped onion
- 2 slices of bread
- Lettuce
- Tomato

Chop the hard-boiled egg. Stir in the Greek yogurt, avocado, and onion. Spread the mixture on one slice of bread. Add the lettuce and tomato and top the sandwich with the second slice of bread.

Beans and Rice
Ingredients

- 1 c. rice (uncooked)
- 2 c. chicken or vegetable broth
- 2 – 15 oz. cans of black beans
- ½ c. of chopped onions
- 1 t. garlic powder
- 1 t. cumin

Cook the rice and onion with the chicken broth as described on the package. Drain and rinse the black beans. When the rice is done, add the beans, cumin, and garlic to the rice.

REBEL Tip: Add some salsa, if desired, for an extra burst of flavor!

Taco Salad
Ingredients

- ½ c. of lean ground beef
- ½ package taco seasoning (low sodium, if preferred)
- 1 ½ c. chopped lettuce
- ½ c. of chopped tomatoes
- ¼ c. chopped onions
- ½ avocado, diced
- ¼ c. salsa
- ¼ c. sour cream (optional)
- ¼ c. shredded cheese
- 2 taco shells (or tortilla chips)

Begin to brown ground beef in saucepan over medium heat. Add taco seasoning when the beef is about halfway cooked. Cook thoroughly. Put the lettuce in a bowl and add the ground beef, tomatoes, onion, avocado, cheese, sour cream, and salsa. If transporting salad for a picnic or for lunch, wrap the taco shells or tortillas separately and add at the last minute.

REBEL Tip: You can brown one pound of ground beef so you can use it with other dishes throughout the week!

Grilled Chicken Quesadilla
Ingredients

- 1 tortilla (8" or 10")
- Chicken strips (use leftovers from another night or pre-cooked grilled chicken strips)
- ¼ c. lettuce
- ¼ c. chopped tomatoes
- ¼ c. chopped onions
- ½ c. shredded cheese
- ¼ c. salsa
- ¼ c. avocado, diced (optional)

Lay the tortilla out on a plate. Sprinkle the cheese on the top half of the tortilla. On the same half of the tortilla top with chicken, lettuce, tomato, onions, cheese, salsa, and avocado. Top with more cheese and fold the tortilla over. Spray a pan with cooking spray, heat pan over medium heat, and then place the tortilla on the pan. Cook on one side until it is brown (about five minutes), then flip to the other side and cook for an additional five minutes.

REBEL Tip: Use a George Foreman® grill or panini press to cook both sides of the tortilla at the same time.

Rotisserie Chicken Honey Raisin Chicken Salad
Ingredients
- ½ c. of diced or shredded rotisserie chicken
- 2 T. Greek yogurt
- 2 T. raisins and/or dried cranberries
- ½ T. honey
- 2 slices of bread

Mix chicken, Greek yogurt, raisins/dried cranberries, and honey. Put on bread and enjoy!

Rotisserie Chicken Basic Chicken Salad
Ingredients
- ½ c. diced or shredded rotisserie chicken
- 2 T. Greek yogurt
- 2 T. chopped onions
- 2 T. chopped tomatoes
- 2 T. celery (optional)
- Pepper to flavor
- 2 slices of bread
- Lettuce leaves
- 1 slice of cheese of your choice

Combine all ingredients in a bowl. Put on bread and top with lettuce and cheese.

REBEL Tip: Purchase a full rotisserie chicken at the grocery store and use throughout the week!

Quinoa Surprise
Ingredients
- Handful of spinach leaves
- ½ c. cooked quinoa
- ½ zucchini, sliced
- 10 stalks asparagus
- 1 Portobello mushroom, sliced
- ½ c. chickpeas
- 1 T. sunflower seeds (or flax seeds)
- Olive oil or nonstick cooking spray
- Salt and pepper, to taste

Cut up some of the fresh spinach leaves and place in bowl. Cook the quinoa (or use microwavable frozen quinoa) and put on top of the spinach leaves. Sauté the asparagus, Portobello mushroom, and zucchini in large sauté pan. Once cooked, add the vegetables on top of the quinoa and spinach. Next, add the chickpeas and seeds of your choice. Add dressing, salt, and pepper to taste.

Dinner

Baked Potato
Ingredients
- 1 baked potato per person

Scrub each potato clean. Use a fork to make a few holes in the skin. Microwave on high for five minutes. Turn potato over and microwave on high for another five minutes. Take out of microwave and serve as desired.

Baked Potato with Chili
Ingredients
- Baked potato (prepared as above)
- 1 t. oil
- 1 yellow onion, chopped
- 1 green pepper, chopped
- 2 cloves garlic, minced
- 1 pound lean ground beef or turkey
- 1 – 14.5 oz. can diced tomatoes with chili pepper
- 2 – 14.5 oz. cans diced tomatoes
- 1 – 8 oz. can tomato sauce
- 1 c. beef or chicken broth
- 1 – 15 oz. can kidney beans
- 1 – 15 oz. can pinto beans
- 2 T. chili powder
- 1 T. ground cumin
- 2 T. white sugar
- 1 T. salt
- 1 t. ground black pepper
- Chili toppings (sour cream, shredded cheese, green onions, etc.)

Heat one teaspoon of oil in large stockpot over medium high heat. When hot, add onion and pepper, then sauté until translucent and soft. Add garlic cloves and cook until fragrant. Add the ground meat, breaking into clumps; cook until browned. Add the rest of the ingredients and simmer for 30 minutes. When ready to serve, cut the baked potato in half, and pour chili on top of the potato. Top with desired toppings. Leftover chili can be stored in containers and frozen for a quick meal.

Potato with Cheese and Broccoli
Ingredients
- ½ c. steamed broccoli florets
- ¼ c. shredded cheddar cheese
- Baked potato

Prepare baked potato as instructed on page 116. When ready to serve, cut potato in half, take steamed broccoli florets, and place it on the potato. Top with as much shredded cheese as desired. Return to microwave for 30 seconds until cheese melts.

Baked Potato with Roasted Chicken
Ingredients
- Chicken breast
- 2 T. Italian dressing or your favorite marinade or seasoning
- Baked potato

Season or marinade the chicken as desired. Bake chicken breast at 400 °F for 20 - 30 minutes until chicken is no longer pink. When you finish making the baked potato, slice it in half and season it with a pat of butter, salt and pepper. Serve the chicken with the potato and a side salad with a dressing of your choice.

Grilled Cheese and Soup
Ingredients
- 2 slices of bread
- Butter
- 1–2 slices of your favorite cheese
- 1 c. tomato soup or any other soup you prefer

Heat a skillet to medium heat. Butter one side of both slices of bread. Place one slice, butter side down onto the heated skillet. Place cheese slices on top, and then top with another bread slice, butter side up. Let bread toast, and cheese melt until the bread is golden brown, about five minutes. Flip the sandwich over so that the other slice of bread has a chance to toast. Watch sandwich carefully and remove from heat when it is the perfect shade of golden brown. Slice in half, and enjoy!

REBEL Tip: Add slices of turkey or ham to your sandwich for an extra protein kick.

Chicken Panini
Ingredients
- 2 slices whole wheat bread
- 1 T. pesto
- 1 oz. slice of mozzarella cheese
- ½ c. cooked chicken
- 2 T. roasted red pepper

Preheat oven to 400 °F. Place both slices of bread on a sheet pan. Spread pesto on one slice. Layer chicken and roasted red pepper. Top with cheese. Place in oven and toast until cheese melts, about 10 minutes. Take out of oven, place the pieces of bread together and enjoy!

REBEL Tip: This could be made in the toaster oven to make it office friendly! Just keep an eye on it while it toasts. Make this panini with spinach, roasted tomato, and pesto for another tasty sandwich option!

BBQ Chicken Quesadilla
Ingredients
- 1 large burrito sized tortilla
- ½ c. shredded cheddar cheese
- ½ c. shredded or cubed cooked chicken
- ¼ c. BBQ sauce

Heat a large skillet on medium-low heat. Place tortilla in skillet; sprinkle half of it with cheese. Top with chicken, BBQ sauce, and the rest of the cheese. Fold tortilla in half and let cook until cheese melts, about five minutes. Flip the tortilla and let other side brown. Serve immediately.

REBEL Tip: Add vegetables like sautéed peppers and onions—even beans!

Tuna Salad

Ingredients

- 1 – 12 oz. can tuna, drained
- ¼ c. mayonnaise, more if you like a creamy tuna salad
- Juice of ½ lemon, more if desired
- ¼ c. chopped red onion
- ¼ c. chopped green onion, white parts and some of the green parts
- ½ T. chopped fresh basil
- ½ T. chopped fresh cilantro
- ½ T. chopped fresh flat-leaf parsley
- ½ t. chopped fresh mint
- ½ T. red wine vinegar
- Salt and freshly ground black pepper

In a large bowl, break up the tuna with a fork and add the mayonnaise, lemon juice, red onions, green onions, basil, cilantro, parsley, mint, and vinegar. Mix well to combine. Taste and season with salt, pepper, and extra lemon juice and mayonnaise as desired.

Tuna Melt

Ingredients

- Tuna Salad (recipe above)
- 3 T. unsalted butter, softened
- 8 slices sourdough bread
- 8 slices cheddar cheese

Brush the softened butter on one side of each slice of bread, setting aside some butter for cooking the sandwiches. Place the bread buttered-side down on a baking sheet. Divide the tuna among four slices of bread and top each with two slices of cheese. Complete the sandwiches with the remaining four slices of bread, buttered-side up. Heat a large nonstick skillet over medium-high heat and add half of the remaining butter. When the butter melts, place two sandwiches in the pan and cook until toasted and golden brown on each side. Repeat with the remaining sandwiches. (If your pan is large enough, you can cook all the sandwiches at the same time.) Serve warm.

Stir-fry
Ingredients

- ½ c. (3 to 4 oz.) of protein (beef, chicken, shrimp, tofu)
- ½ to 1 c. of vegetables
- Sauce, to taste (based on personal preferences)
- ½ to 1 c. of starch (noodles or rice—already cooked)

Heat a wok or large sauce pan with oil on medium high heat. Cut vegetables into small pieces. Throw into the wok and start stirring. Take your desired protein and cut into bite-sized pieces. Season with salt and pepper. Once the vegetables have started to soften, add the protein into the hot wok. Stir constantly for 2 to 3 minutes. Once the protein and vegetables are cooked through and browned, you may add the starch to the pan in the last few minutes of cooking, or decide to continue to the last step and serve the starch on the side. Once everything has reached your desired level of doneness, add sauce and sauté for a few more minutes.

REBEL Tip: Stir-fry chicken breasts with broccoli and sauce of choice. Serve over brown rice. You can also mix black beans with rice, vegetables, and tofu for a vegetarian stir-fry. For more ideas see the stir-fry infographic in Chapter 2, page 47.

Pasta Salad with Vegetables and Italian Dressing
Ingredients

- 1 box of uncooked short pasta (any shape is fine)
- ½ c. thinly sliced carrots
- 2 stalks of celery, chopped
- ½ c. chopped green bell pepper
- ½ c. cucumber, peeled and thinly sliced
- 2 large tomatoes, diced
- ¼ c. chopped onion
- 2 – 16 oz. bottles of Italian-style dressing
- ½ c. Parmesan cheese

Heat large stockpot of water to boiling. Add salt if desired. Cook pasta in boiling water until al dente. Rinse under cold water to stop cooking and drain. Mix chopped carrots, celery, cucumber, green pepper, tomatoes, and onion together in a large bowl. Combine cooled pasta and vegetables in the bowl. Pour Italian dressing over the mixture. Add Parmesan cheese and mix well. Chill one hour before serving.

Pasta with Grilled Vegetables
Ingredients

- 16 oz. box pasta, uncooked, any shape
- Olive oil
- 1 T. fresh basil, chopped
- ½ t. dried oregano
- 2 c. favorite grilled/roasted vegetables
- Parmesan cheese

Bring a large stockpot of water to a boil. Add salt and a splash of oil. Add pasta and cook per box instructions. Once pasta is done, drain off water using a colander and set aside. Heat a large sauté pan on medium high heat and add two teaspoons of olive oil. When hot, add the pasta to the pan. Add the basil, oregano, and grilled vegetables. Mix well until everything is heated, about five minutes. Top with Parmesan cheese and serve.

One-Pot Italian Pasta (Serves 6)
Ingredients

- 4 c. vegetable broth
- 2 T. olive oil
- 12 oz. fettuccine pasta
- 8 oz. frozen chopped spinach
- 1 – 28 oz. can diced tomatoes
- 1 medium onion, thinly sliced
- 4 cloves garlic, thinly sliced
- ½ T. dried basil
- ½ T. dried oregano
- ¼ t. red pepper flakes
- Freshly cracked pepper to taste
- 2 oz. feta cheese

Add vegetable broth to a large pot. Break the fettuccine in half (it helps to make stirring easier later) and then add it to the pot. Add un-drained canned tomatoes, olive oil, frozen spinach, onion (thinly sliced), garlic (thinly sliced), basil, oregano, red pepper flakes, and some freshly cracked black pepper. Make sure the ingredients are submerged under the liquid. Place a lid on the pot and turn the heat on high. Allow the pot to come to a full, rolling boil; remove the lid and reduce heat to medium.

Allow the pot to continue to boil over medium heat without a lid for 10 to 15 minutes or until the pasta is cooked and most of the liquid has been absorbed. Stir the pot every few minutes as it cooks to prevent the pasta from sticking to the bottom, but avoid over stirring which can cause the pasta to become sticky and mushy. The pot must be boiling the entire time. After the pasta is cooked, crumble the feta cheese over the top and serve!

REBEL Tip: Round out the meal by serving this with roasted chicken breast and a side salad.

Spaghetti Sauce with Parmesan Cheese
Ingredients

- 2 lbs. Italian sausage, casings removed (mild or hot)
- 1 small onion, chopped (optional)
- 3–4 garlic cloves, minced
- 1 – 28 oz. cans diced tomatoes
- 2 – 6 oz. cans tomato paste
- 2 – 15 oz. cans tomato sauce
- 2 c. water (less if you will be simmering for a shorter period of time)
- 3 t. basil
- 2 t. dried parsley flakes
- 1 ½ t. brown sugar
- 1 t. salt
- ¼–½ t. crushed red pepper flakes
- ¼ t. fresh coarse ground black pepper
- ¼ c. red wine (try a good Cabernet!)
- 1 lb. thin spaghetti
- Parmesan cheese

In a large, heavy stockpot, brown Italian sausage, breaking up as you stir. Add onions and continue to cook, stirring occasionally until onions are softened. Add garlic, tomatoes, tomato paste, tomato sauce and water. Add basil, parsley, brown sugar, salt, crushed red pepper, and black pepper. Stir well and barely bring to a boil. Stir in red wine. Simmer on low, stirring frequently for at least an hour. A longer simmer makes for a better sauce—just be careful not to let it burn!

Cook spaghetti according to package directions. Spoon sauce over drained spaghetti noodles and sprinkle with Parmesan cheese

REBEL Tip: This recipe lends itself to be REBELized very easily! Serve this sauce with spaghetti, baked ziti, and lasagna. The possibilities are endless! You can also make this in a slow cooker. Place all of the sauce ingredients in the slow cooker and heat on low for six hours. You can also double the batch and freeze the extra for a quick dinner on a weeknight!

Pizza Dough
Ingredients
- 1 pack of yeast
- 1 t. of sugar
- 1 c. warm water
- 2 ½ c. all purpose or whole wheat flour
- 1 t. salt
- 2 T. olive oil

Combine yeast, sugar, and water in a measuring cup. Let sit for 10 minutes until bubbly. Mix yeast mixture with flour, salt, and oil. Knead until smooth. Let rest for five minutes. Preheat the oven to 450 °F. Pat or roll dough into a round or square pizza. Top with desired toppings and bake for 15 to 20 minutes until golden brown.

Pizza Sauce
Ingredients
- 1 t. olive oil
- 1 medium yellow onion, diced
- 1 clove of garlic
- 1 – 28 oz. can of crushed tomatoes
- 1 t. basil
- ½ t. Italian seasoning

Heat olive oil in a stock pot over medium heat. Add diced onion and sauté until translucent. Add garlic and cook until fragrant. Add tomatoes, basil, and Italian seasoning. Turn down to low and simmer for 20 minutes. Use for pizza and freeze leftovers!

REBEL Tip: Take the REBEL Pizza Challenge in Chapter 2, page 48.

Mini Pizzas
Ingredients
- English muffin (or bagel)
- ½ c. tomato sauce, jar or homemade
- ½ c. shredded mozzarella cheese
- Spinach (or other vegetable of choice—chopped broccoli, peppers, onions, mushrooms, olives)
- Turkey pepperoni (optional)

Toast the English muffin or bagel in toaster oven for a minute or two until slightly brown. Spread on the sauce and add the cheese. Top with spinach (or other vegetables) and turkey pepperoni. Toast again in toaster oven or bake at 400 °F until the cheese gets bubbly.

Grilled Chicken Parmesan
Ingredients
- 4 chicken breasts
- 2 c. (plus more for spaghetti) tomato sauce, homemade or store bought
- ¼ c. mozzarella cheese, grated
- 1 c. cooked spaghetti

Season each chicken breast with salt and pepper on each side. Heat grill or grill pan to medium heat. Make sure to use grill spray. Cook chicken breasts until done, about eight minutes on each side. You can also roast in the oven at 400 °F for 20 to 30 minutes until chicken is no longer pink.

While the chicken is cooking, warm up the tomato sauce. When ready to eat, top each chicken breast with ½ cup tomato sauce. Top each with two tablespoons of mozzarella cheese. Turn on the broiler, and place chicken under it until melted and bubbly.

Serve chicken with spaghetti topped with additional sauce if desired.

Crispy Chicken Tenders with Buffalo Sauce and Salad
Ingredients
- ¼ c. all-purpose flour
- 1 egg
- 1 T. water
- Salt and pepper to taste
- 1 c. plain or Italian-style, panko crispy breadcrumbs
- ½ c. grated Parmesan cheese
- 1–1 ¼ lb. uncooked chicken breast tenders or chicken breasts cut into strips.

Heat oven to 425 °F. Line cookie sheet with foil; spray with cooking spray. Place flour in a shallow dish. In second shallow dish, beat egg and water. In third shallow dish, mix breadcrumbs and cheese. Season chicken with salt and pepper, then coat with flour. Dip floured chicken into egg mixture, then coat with breadcrumb mixture. Place on foil-lined cookie sheet.

Bake 15 to 20 minutes, turning once, until chicken is no longer pink in center and coating is golden brown. Serve tenders with a salad. Top with buffalo sauce and your favorite dressing.

Chicken Kabobs (makes 8 skewers, serves 4)

Ingredients

- 8 – 12 in. bamboo skewers
- 1 lb. chicken breasts, cut into bite-sized pieces
- Italian dressing
- 2 medium zucchini
- ½ lb. mushrooms
- 1 red pepper

Soak the skewers in water while you prepare the rest of the ingredients. This ensures they won't burn in the oven or on the grill. Marinate chicken in Italian dressing for 30 to 60 minutes. Chop the vegetables into bite-sized pieces that are similar in size to the chicken. This will ensure everything cooks at the same rate. (Smaller mushrooms might not need to be cut.)

Preheat oven to 400 ^{0}F or preheat grill using medium heat. Assemble skewers, alternating the vegetables and the chicken. Grill or bake the kabobs for 20 minutes or until chicken is done.

REBEL Tip: Use any vegetables that you like! You can also experiment with seafood and other kinds of meat.

Burger with Carrot Fries

Ingredients

- 2 lbs. lean ground beef or turkey
- Salt and pepper to taste (for burger)
- Burger toppings (cheese, mayo, lettuce, tomato, onions)
- Buns
- 2 lbs. carrots
- 1 T. olive oil
- Salt and pepper to taste (for carrot fries)

Preheat oven to 425 ^{0}F. Peel and slice carrots into French fry shaped pieces (about ½" x ½" x 3"). Toss carrots with olive oil, salt, and pepper. Arrange carrots in a single layer on baking sheet. Bake for 10 minutes then flip each carrot fry. Continue to bake until fully cooked and slightly crispy, about 10 more minutes.

Meanwhile, divide ground beef into four portions. Shape into burger patties. Season each side with salt and pepper. Heat a grill pan, outdoor grill or regular sauté pan. Cook burger to desired doneness, about five to six minutes for medium well. Top with cheese and other desired toppings. Serve on bun with carrot fries.

REBEL Tip: You can also make fries with other root vegetables like parsnips!

Meatballs
Ingredients
- 1 lb. lean (at least 80%) ground beef
- ½ Italian-style breadcrumbs
- ¼ c. milk
- ½ t. salt
- ½ t. Worcestershire sauce
- ¼ t. pepper
- 1 small onion, finely chopped (¼ c.)
- 1 egg

Preheat oven to 400 °F. Line 13 x 9-inch pan with foil; spray with cooking spray. In large bowl, mix all ingredients. Shape mixture into 20 to 24 (1½ inch) meatballs. Place one inch apart in pan. Bake uncovered for 18 to 22 minutes or until no longer pink in center.

REBEL Tip: Serve with marinara sauce and spaghetti! You can also make your own meatball subs. Try serving these meatballs with whole wheat pasta, basil, and olive oil.

Meatloaf in Muffin Tins
Ingredients
- 1 ¾ pounds ground sirloin
- 1 medium onion, cut into chunks
- 2 ribs celery from the heart of the stalk, cut into 2-inch pieces
- 1 green bell pepper
- 1 large egg plus a splash of milk, beaten
- 1 c. plain breadcrumbs
- 2 T. grill seasoning (recommended: Montreal Steak Seasoning by McCormick)
- 1 c. smoky barbecue sauce
- ½ c. tomato salsa
- 1 T. Worcestershire sauce
- Vegetable oil or extra-virgin olive oil

Preheat oven to 450 °F. Put ground beef into a big bowl. Put onion and celery into a food processor. Cut the bell pepper in half and remove seeds. Cut the pepper into a few pieces and add to the food processor. Pulse the processor blades to finely chop the vegetables into very small pieces. Add them to the meat bowl. Add egg with milk mixture, breadcrumbs, and grill seasoning to the bowl. Next, combine smoky barbecue sauce, salsa, and Worcestershire sauce. Pour half the sauce mixture into the bowl with the meatloaf mix. Mix the meatloaf together with your hands. Wash hands. Brush a 12 muffin tin (½ cup each) with vegetable oil or extra-virgin olive oil. Use an ice cream scoop to help you fill meat into each tin. Top each meat loaf with a spoonful of extra sauce. Bake about 20 minutes. Cut open one muffin to test that the middle is cooked through.

Black Bean Nachos
Ingredients
- Tortilla chips
- 1 – 15 oz. can black beans
- 3 c. shredded cheese
- 1 c. salsa
- 1 avocado, cubed
- Shredded lettuce, other desired toppings

Preheat the broiler; spread the tortilla chips in a single layer on a baking sheet. Drain the black beans and distribute evenly over the chips. Sprinkle shredded cheese over the beans and chips. Place under the broiler until cheese is melted and bubbly. (Watch nachos carefully to prevent burning.)

When cheese is melted, remove from oven, top with salsa, avocado, and other desired toppings. Serve immediately.

Black Bean Burgers
Ingredients
- ½ medium yellow onion, roughly chopped
- 1 T. chopped garlic
- 2 – 15 oz. cans black beans, rinsed and drained, divided
- 2 T. freshly chopped cilantro leaves
- 2 t. freshly chopped parsley leaves
- 1 egg
- ½ t. red pepper flakes
- ½ c. breadcrumbs
- Salt and fresh ground black pepper
- 4 hamburger rolls

Optional Toppings:
- 1 tomato, sliced
- 4 small Romaine lettuce leaves (or any other type you have on hand)
- ¼ c. ketchup

Heat a grill or grill pan over medium-low heat. In a food processor, pulse onion and garlic until finely chopped. Add one can of black beans, cilantro, parsley, egg, and red pepper flakes. Pulse to combine. Transfer mixture to a large mixing bowl; add the remaining can of black beans and the breadcrumbs. Season with salt and pepper—to taste—and mix until well combined. Divide mixture into four and form into patties. Place on hot oiled grill over medium-low heat and cook about six minutes per side or until heated through. Toast hamburger buns on a grill. Place a burger on the bottom of each bun. Top with lettuce, tomato, and ketchup. Cover the burgers with the top of the bun and serve.

✳ Black Bean Dip

Ingredients

- ¼ c. extra-virgin olive oil
- 2 small yellow onions, chopped
- 4 cloves garlic, peeled and chopped into large chunks
- 2 jalapeño peppers, seeded and chopped
- 2 – 15.5 oz. cans black beans, rinsed and drained
- 1 ½ t. salt
- ½ t. ground cumin
- 2 T. fresh lime juice, from one lime, plus more if desired
- 3 T. water
- ¼ c. fresh chopped cilantro, plus more for garnish (optional)

Heat the olive oil over medium heat in a small saucepan. Add the onions, garlic, and jalapeño peppers. Cook, stirring occasionally, until very soft, about ten minutes. Do not brown.

Transfer the cooked onion mixture to a blender or food processor and add the black beans, salt, cumin, lime juice, water, and cilantro. Blend until smooth. (If using a blender, you may need to stop and stir a few times to help it out.) If the dip is too thick, add more water or lime juice little by little to thin. Taste and adjust seasoning, then transfer to a serving bowl.

Serve warm, cold, or room temperature with tortilla chips, pita chips, or vegetables.

REBEL Tip: Most of the heat from the jalapeños is in the seeds and ribs, so leave those out. If you like a spicier dip, reserve the seeds and add them little by little when you are blending the dip.

✳ Last-Minute Black Bean Soup (4 Servings)

Ingredients

- 1 – 19 oz. can black beans, un-drained
- 1 ½ c. frozen corn kernels
- ½ c. salsa
- ½ c. water
- 1 T. bottled or fresh lime juice
- ½ to 1 t. chili powder
- ½ to 1 t. ground cumin
- ¼ c. shredded, reduced-fat cheddar cheese
- ½ c. reduced-fat sour cream, optional

✳ Make in muffin tin freeze & put in a bag for later.

In a medium saucepan, combine the beans, corn, salsa, water, lime juice, chili powder, and cumin. Cover and bring to a boil. Reduce the heat and simmer, uncovered, about five minutes. Serve in individual bowls and top with the cheese and sour cream as desired.

REBEL Tip: This soup will warm you up and would be excellent with a fresh salad or sandwich!

Grilled Fish Tacos (4 servings)
Ingredients
- 1 mango, peeled, pitted, and cubed
- 1 avocado, pitted, peeled, and cubed
- ½ red onion, finely chopped
- 2 limes
- Chopped fresh cilantro
- Salt and black pepper
- Canola oil
- 2 large (about 16 oz.) mahi mahi fillet (or any white-fleshed fish)
- 1 T. blackening spice
- 8 corn tortillas
- 2 c. finely shredded red cabbage

Mix mango, avocado, onion, and juice of one lime in a bowl. Season with cilantro, salt, and pepper. Heat a grill or stovetop grill pan until hot. Drizzle a light coating of oil over the fish and rub on the blackening spice. Cook the fish undisturbed for four minutes. Carefully flip with spatula and cook for another four minutes. Remove from heat.

Warm tortillas on the grill for one to two minutes or wrap in damp paper towels and microwave for one minute until warm and pliable. Break fish into chunks and divide among the warm tortillas. Top with cabbage and the mango salsa. Serve with wedges from second lime.

REBEL Tip: If mangos aren't in season, peaches or pineapple make great substitutes. You can also make these tacos with shellfish, chicken, or beef.

Roasted Salmon with Salsa and Roasted Vegetables
Ingredients
- 8 oz. salmon, cut into two portions
- ½ c. your favorite salsa (jarred or homemade)
- 2 c. favorite vegetables (1 c. per serving)

Cut all your favorite vegetables into bite-sized pieces. (Make sure all the pieces are about the same size so that they cook at the same rate.) Season as desired and roast at 400 ^{0}F for 35 to 40 minutes, stirring every 15 minutes. While the vegetables roast, place the salmon in a roasting pan; top with salsa. Bake for 12 to 15 minutes at 400 ^{0}F until desired doneness. Serve salmon with roasted vegetables.

✳ Salmon Cakes (4 servings, 3 cakes per serving)
Ingredients
- 2 strips bacon, cooked crispy
- ¼ c. chopped onion
- 1 egg
- ½ c. mayonnaise
- 2 t. Dijon mustard
- ½ t. sugar
- 1 t. lemon zest
- 1 – 14 oz. can wild salmon, checked for large bones
- 1 baked or boiled russet potato, peeled, and fluffed with a fork
- ¼ c. breadcrumbs
- 2 T. grated Parmesan cheese
- Freshly ground black pepper, to taste
- ½ c. vegetable oil

Crumble bacon and reserve bacon fat. Heat one tablespoon of reserved bacon fat in a small sauté pan over low heat. Add onions and cook until translucent. Slightly cool onions. Mix bacon, onion, egg, mayonnaise, mustard, sugar, and lemon zest in a bowl. Add salmon and potato, mixing gently after each addition. Form the mixture into 12 small patties.

In a shallow dish, combine breadcrumbs, Parmesan cheese, and pepper. Coat the patties in breadcrumb topping. Heat ¼ c. of the oil in a large sauté pan over medium heat, and cook the salmon cakes in batches until golden, about three to four minutes per side. Add more oil, as necessary. Arrange on a serving platter and serve with a garden salad or other desired vegetables.

REBEL Tip: Remove bacon and just use a little bit of oil if you wish to lower saturated fat.

Teriyaki Salmon with Snap Peas (4 servings)
Ingredients

- 2 T. brown sugar
- 2 T. low-sodium soy sauce
- 1 t. finely grated orange zest
- 1 – 6 oz. can pineapple juice
- ½ t. salt, divided
- 2 t. canola oil
- 4 – 6 oz. salmon fillets (about 1 inch thick)
- ¼ t. freshly ground black pepper
- Grated orange rind (optional)

Combine brown sugar, soy sauce, orange zest, pineapple juice and ¼ teaspoon salt in a small saucepan over high heat, and bring to a boil. Reduce heat, and simmer until reduced to ¼ cup (about 15 minutes). Set aside.

Preheat oven to 400 °F. Heat oil in a large nonstick skillet over medium-high heat. Sprinkle both sides of salmon with remaining ¼ t. salt and black pepper. Add fish to pan; cook three minutes. Turn fish over and place in oven. Bake at 400 °F for three minutes. Remove from oven; brush one tablespoon sauce over each fillet. Return to oven, and cook one minute or until fish flakes easily when tested with a fork or until desired degree of doneness.

Sprinkle with orange rind, if desired. Serve with steamed snap peas.

Salmon Chowder (4 servings)

Ingredients

- 4 slices bacon, chopped
- 6 shallots, chopped
- 1/3 c. chopped fresh dill
- 3 medium Yukon gold potatoes, peeled and diced
- 6 medium carrots, diced
- Kosher salt
- 1 – 10 oz. package sliced white mushrooms
- 10 oz. Brussels sprouts, halved (quartered if large)
- 2 large egg yolks
- 1 c. half-and-half
- 3 T. dry white wine or fresh lemon juice
- ¾ pound skinless salmon fillet, cut into 2-inch pieces
- Freshly ground pepper

Cook the bacon in a large saucepan over medium heat until crisp, about five minutes. Drain the bacon drippings until about one teaspoon is left. Stir in the shallots and half of the dill; cook until the shallots are soft, about three minutes. Add potatoes, carrots, four cups water, and one teaspoon salt. Increase the heat to medium high, cover, and bring to a simmer. Cook until the potatoes and carrots are almost tender, about six minutes. Add mushrooms and Brussels sprouts and cook until all of the vegetables are tender, about six minutes.

Meanwhile, whisk the egg yolks, half-and-half, and wine in a small bowl. Reduce the heat to medium low. Add the salmon and cook until opaque, two to three minutes. Gently stir in the egg mixture and cook until the soup thickens slightly, one to two minutes. Season with salt and pepper. Divide among bowls and top with the remaining dill.

Salad

Ingredients

- 2 c. of lettuce
- ¼ c. of a variety of vegetables to mix in salad
- ½ c. protein (meat, cheese, etc…)
- ½ c. carbohydrate topping
- 2 T. dressing

Place all desired ingredients in a bowl, and top with dressing. Toss together and eat!

Snacks

No-Bake Energy Bites (Makes about 20 to 25 balls)
Ingredients
- 1 c. dry, old-fashioned oatmeal
- ⅔ c. toasted coconut flakes
- ½ c. peanut butter (or any kind of nut butter)
- ½ c. ground flax seeds
- ½ c. chocolate chips or cacao nibs (optional)
- ⅓ c. honey (can also use other sweetener like agave or maple syrup)
- 1 T. chia seeds (optional)
- 1 t. vanilla extract

Stir all ingredients together in a medium bowl until thoroughly mixed. Cover and let chill in the refrigerator for half an hour. Once chilled, roll into one-inch balls (you can make them any size you like). Store in an airtight container and keep refrigerated for up to one week.

REBEL Tip: If you start experimenting with different ingredients or leave some ingredients out, the balance of the recipe may be a little off. If mixture is too dry, add a few more of the sticky ingredients like honey and/or peanut butter. If it is too gooey, add in more oats.

Sweet Potato Nachos ✳
Ingredients
- 1 sweet potato, thinly sliced

Optional nacho toppings
- Black beans
- Chicken
- Tomatoes
- Cheese
- Avocado
- Onion
- Red pepper
- Lettuce

Preheat oven to 425 °F. Lay sweet potato slices on a Silpat® nonstick sheet or greased baking sheet. Spray with olive oil and sprinkle with desired spices: paprika, cayenne pepper, cumin, etc.

Bake for 20 to 30 minutes or until crispy, flipping every 10 minutes. Watch chips closely at the end and remove those that are getting too dark. Add toppings and return to the oven to melt the cheese.

Date Snack Bars
Ingredients
- 2 c. of pitted dates
- ¾ c. raw cashews
- ⅓ c. peanut butter
- ½ c. unsweetened shredded coconut
- 2 T. cocoa powder
- Pinch of salt

Place all ingredients in a food processor and mix until ingredients become smooth and clump into a ball. Place mixture into an 8-inch square pan lined with parchment paper. Use your hands to press mixture firmly onto the bottom of the pan.

Cover and refrigerate for 30 minutes. Remove mixture from dish and cut into bars using a sharp knife. Store in an air-tight container in the refrigerator or freezer.

Roasted Chickpeas
Ingredients
- 2 – 15 oz. cans of chickpeas, drained
- 1 T. olive oil
- ½ T. of garlic powder
- ½ T. of cayenne pepper (optional)

Preheat the oven to 450 °F. Drain and rinse the chickpeas, then blot with a paper towel to dry. Mix together chickpeas, olive oil, garlic powder, and cayenne pepper. Lay out on a sheet pan. Bake in the oven for about 30 to 40 minutes until the chickpeas get the desired crunch. The longer you bake them, the crunchier the chickpeas will be.

Guacamole (2 servings)
Ingredients
- 1 avocado
- ¼ c. chopped onions
- ¼ c. diced tomatoes
- 2 T. fresh cilantro, chopped (optional)
- Lime juice from ½ large lime
- Salt and pepper, to taste

Mash the avocado in a large bowl. Add in the onion, tomato, and cilantro. Mix together. Add in the lime juice and mix. Add salt and pepper to taste.

Hummus
Ingredients
- 2 c. of chickpeas, drained
- ⅓ c. tahini
- ¼ c. lemon juice
- 1 t. salt
- 2 cloves of garlic
- 1 T. olive oil
- 1 t. paprika

Place the chickpeas, tahini, lemon juice, salt, and garlic in a blender or food processor. Blend on high until the mixture is creamy. Drizzle with olive oil and paprika.

REBEL Tip: Use cut, fresh vegetables as "dippers!"

Kale Chips
Ingredients
- 1 bunch of kale
- 1 T. of olive oil
- 1 t. garlic powder
- 1 t. black pepper
- 1 t. red pepper flakes (optional)
- 1 t. salt

Preheat the oven to 300 °F. Remove the kale leaves from the stem and rinse them in cool water. Put the kale in a large bowl and add the olive oil and spices. Mix until the kale leaves are evenly coated in the olive oil and spices. Spread the kale out on a sheet pan. Bake in the oven for about 15 minutes. Rotate the pan and bake for an additional 10 minutes.

Sweet Potato Fries
Ingredients
- 2 large sweet potatoes
- 1 T. olive oil
- Salt and pepper to taste.

Preheat the oven to 450 °F. Cut the sweet potatoes in half. Continue to cut lengthways until the sweet potatoes are in a fry-like shape. Mix the olive oil, spices, and sweet potato in a bowl until the sweet potatoes are evenly coated.

Bake in the oven for 15 minutes. Take out of the oven and stir the sweet potatoes. Bake for another 20 minutes, longer for crispier fries.

Banana and Peanut Butter Whip
Ingredients
- 1 frozen banana, peeled
- 2 T. peanut butter (may substitute other nut butters)
- 1 t. of cocoa powder
- ¼ c. of chocolate chips
- 2 T. coconut flakes (optional)
- 1 T. flax or chia seeds (optional)

Cut the frozen banana in half. Place it in a blender or food processor. Add in peanut butter and chocolate chips/cocoa powder. Blend until all the ingredients are mixed together and the mixture is smooth.

Hot Chocolate (4 servings)
Ingredients
- ⅓ c. cocoa powder
- ¾ c. sugar
- ⅓ c. boiling water
- 4 c. of milk
- ¾ t. vanilla extract
- Mini marshmallows (optional)

Combine the cocoa, sugar, and boiling water in a pot on the stove. Bring the mixture to a boil, and let simmer for two minutes, while stirring occasionally. Add in the milk and continue to heat for another five minutes or so. Remove the mixture from the heat and add the vanilla. Top it off with marshmallows!

Peanut Butter, Strawberry, and Banana Quesadilla
Ingredients
- 1 tortilla
- 2 T. peanut butter
- ½ c. of strawberries, sliced
- ½ banana, sliced
- Cinnamon

Spread the peanut butter evenly on the tortilla. Place the banana and strawberry slices on one side of the tortilla. Sprinkle with cinnamon. Fold over the tortilla. Spray pan with cooking spray, heat over medium, and place the tortilla on the pan. Cook for two minutes on one side, then flip and cook for two minutes on the other side. You may need to flip again, depending on how crispy you like the tortilla.

REBEL Tip: Try using a George Foreman® grill or panini press to cook the quesadilla.

Grilled Peanut Butter and Banana Sandwich
Ingredients
- 2 slices of whole grain bread
- 2 T. peanut butter
- ½ banana, sliced
- Dash cinnamon, if desired
- 1 t. honey, if desired
- 2 T. of raisins or dried cranberries, if desired

Spread one tablespoon peanut butter on each slice of bread. Put the banana slices on the bread and put the other slice of bread on top of the one that has the banana slices. Add cinnamon, honey, and/or dried fruit if desired. Spray pan with cooking spray, heat over medium, and place the sandwich on the pan. Cook for two minutes on one side, then flip and cook for two minutes on the other side. You may need to flip again, depending on how crispy you like the bread.

REBEL Tip: Try using a George Foreman® grill or panini press to cook the sandwich.

Baked Apples or Pears with Cinnamon
Ingredients
- 1 apple or pear
- ¼ t. cinnamon
- ½ T. honey
- ½ t. vanilla extract
- 1 T. of nut butter (optional)

Core the apple (pear), but leave the bottom intact. Stir together the cinnamon, honey, nut butter, and vanilla, then add to the middle of the apple (or pear). Bake for about three and a half to four minutes in the microwave.

REBEL Tip: If you would like to make more than one baked apple, you can easily make two or three in the microwave for the family. You can also make a bunch of baked apples (or pears) in the oven. Preheat the oven to 375 °F. Bake the apples (or pears) for 30 to 45 minutes.

Trail Mix
Ingredients
- ¼ c. almonds
- 2 T. chocolate chips
- ¼ c. raisins or dried cranberries
- ½ c. Honey Nut Cheerios®

Combine all ingredients together and enjoy!

Food Log (Copy as needed)

Time	Hunger	Mood Before	Food, Amount, and Environment	Satiety	Mood After
			Breakfast:		
			Snack:		
			Lunch:		
			Snack:		
			Dinner:		
			Snack:		

Food Adjectives

acidic	fibrous	delicious	crumbly
dry	brittle	airy	crispy
bold	nutty	blah	crunchy
dull	fragrant	crusty	disagreeable
delectable	bland	fresh	earthy
cheesy	creamy	fizzy	flavorless
fluffy	fried	hearty	lumpy
mild	nasty	savory	seasoned
sour	spicy	starchy	stringy
tangy	sweet	strong	tart

Main Principles of Health at Every Size (HAES)

(Adapted from https://www.sizediversityandhealth.org/content.asp?id=76)

1. **Weight Inclusivity:** Accept and respect the inherent diversity of body shapes and sizes and reject the idealizing or pathologizing of specific weights.
2. **Health Enhancement:** Support health policies that improve and equalize access to information and services, and personal practices that improve human well-being, including attention to individual physical, economic, social, spiritual, emotional, and other needs.
3. **Respectful Care:** Acknowledge our biases, and work to end weight discrimination, weight stigma, and weight bias. Provide information and services from an understanding that socio-economic status, race, gender, sexual orientation, age, and other identities impact weight stigma, and support environments that address these inequities.
4. **Eating for Well-Being:** Promote flexible, individualized eating based on hunger, satiety, nutritional needs, and pleasure, rather than any externally regulated eating plan focused on weight control.
5. **Life-Enhancing Movement:** Support physical activities that allow people of all sizes, abilities, and interests to engage in enjoyable movement, to the degree that they choose.

The Happiness Trap Worksheets: Russ Harris

Your Values: What really matters to you deep in your heart? What do you want to do with your time on this planet? What sort of person do you want to be? What personal strengths or qualities do you want to develop?

1. **Work/Education:** includes workplace, career, education, skills development, etc.
2. **Relationships:** includes your partner, children, parents, relatives, friends, co-workers, and other social contacts.
3. **Personal Growth/Health:** may include religion, spirituality, creativity, life skills, meditation, yoga, nature, exercise, nutrition, and/or addressing health risk factors such as smoking, alcohol, drugs, overeating, etc.
4. **Leisure:** how you play, relax, stimulate, or enjoy yourself; activities for rest, recreation, fun and creativity.

THE BULL'S EYE: Make an X in each area of the dart board to represent where you stand today.

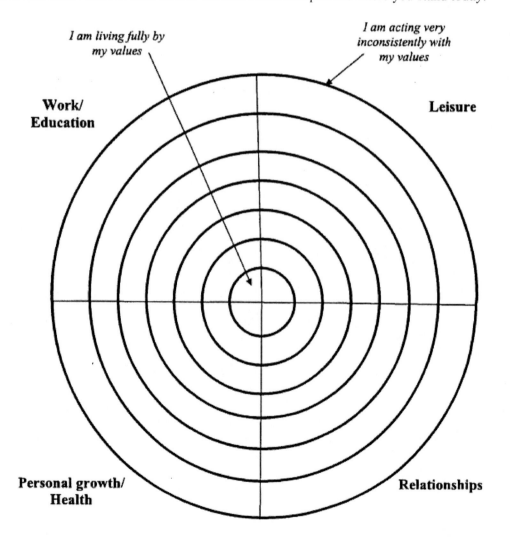

Testimonials

By being a REBEL, you will learn a lot about yourself, nourish your mind and body, feel healthier, and address your weight concerns. Using the non-dieting approach, we will teach you the tools you need to be successful in improving your happiness and health. The truth behind conventional dieting is that it can be restrictive, keeping you from enjoying the food you love, and it is often difficult to maintain. Many people see success at first, but inevitably they find the weight comes back. As you REBEL dieting, you will be able to incorporate the foods you love and find feeding yourself and your family less stressful. As REBEL Dietitians®, we feel nutrition is very important, but it is not the only key to happiness and only deserves a small space in your everyday life. We can help you to put food back in its place, leaving room to better your relationships, stress levels, and fun in your life.

See what our clients are saying:

"My first appointment with Dana was awesome. Dana really opened my eyes to a lot of things concerning my health. Dana is phenomenal! I have an appointment with her today, and I have never been excited about having an appointment."

"My appointment with Kait was very helpful. I came in worried about how it would go, but Kait listened to my concerns, did not once mention weight loss as a possible goal, and gave me good, concrete meal planning advice I was immediately able to take home and use. I am very pleased to be working with Kait, and would not hesitate to recommend her to a friend."

"I love Dana. She is wonderful to work with. Supportive, great listener, great suggestions, non-judgmental, but gently holds you accountable. I am very thankful I was referred to your office!"

"During my first visit Kait put me at ease that there was hope and I could tackle this and get my health back and lose weight. She gave me a great starting point of how to balance my nutritional needs as a diabetic. She listened and guided me to a point where I could understand what I needed to do and how to have the right combinations of food groups to balance my needs. Because of Kait's help, I no longer feel like I'm lost in sea of over information about diabetes and nutrition. I get what I need when I ask questions. She has given me guidance and the tools that I need to be successful. I feel empowered. What was once the drudgery of the diabetic and nutritional maze is now an adventure as I rediscover food in a whole new way. Nutrition, meal planning, and exercise are becoming a journey to a new, healthier, happier me. I look forward to the changes to come from eating well and exercising."

Meet the REBEL Team

KAIT FORTUNATO GREENBERG, RD, LD

Kait Fortunato Greenberg is a registered dietitian working with clients who want to form healthy relationships with food. Kait specializes in binge eating disorder, emotional eating, and restrictive eating disorders. Her program, *REBEL Against Dieting*, helps clients break free from diet prison once and for all!
She helps clients who have been on various diets all of their life and who may be frustrated with the dieting industry for igniting feelings of despair and failure. Kait also enjoys helping children form healthy relationships with food. She tirelessly spreads the non-dieting message, encouraging people to not let food get in the way of what truly matters in their life.

Kait writes about the non-dieting approach using various forms of social media including the *Washingtonian, WTOP Washington DC Healthy Living Section, STACK Media for High School Athletes*, and the *Empowered Eating Blog*. Kait is a member of the Association for Size Diversity and Health, and she supports client health and happiness regardless of body size and shape.

Kait travels around the country to speak about the *REBEL Against Dieting* program, helping clients reclaim their life and overcome their food and weight struggles. She loves connecting with people across the country to help them give up dieting once and for all. In 2013, Kait was named the "Outstanding Young Registered Dietitian of the Year" by the Academy of Nutrition and Dietetics.

Kait is passionate about giving back to the field of dietetics, helping to spread the non-dieting message to other registered dietitians, encouraging them to do what they love and stay true to what they value. Her first book, *Welcome to the REBELUTION: Seven Steps to the Nutrition Counseling Practice of Your Dreams*, encourages registered dietitians to identify their passion, utilize their strengths, and create the practice that aligns with their personal and professional values.

Kait is a proud member of *Behavioral Health Nutrition, a dietetic practice group of the Academy of Nutrition and Dietetics; Sports, Cardiovascular, and Wellness Nutrition, a dietetic practice group of the Academy of Nutrition and Dietetics*; and *Nutrition Entrepreneurs, a dietetic practice group of the Academy of Nutrition and Dietetics*, as well as *the International Federation of Eating Disorder Dietitians*.

DANA MAGEE, RD, LD, CLT

Dana is a registered dietitian who provides individual nutrition counseling sessions with the mission to rebuild her clients' relationship with food. Dana sees clients for overeating, binge eating disorder, restrictive eating, emotional eating, picky eating, polycystic ovarian syndrome, diabetes, food sensitivities, and digestive wellness.

Many of Dana's clients have been on the dieting roller coaster for most of their lives. Not only have these clients experienced weight loss only to gain it back and more, but they suffer from the stress that comes from watching the number on the scale. This is why Dana offers the *REBEL Against Dieting* program.

Whether you have been a lifetime dieter or have just begun to experiment with dieting, Dana can help you learn to nourish your body, improve your health, and limit the stress around food.

Dana's goal is not only to help her clients improve their nutrition knowledge and create healthy habits, but also to improve their quality of life and conquer their disordered eating. Dana is passionate about supporting her clients with the tools they need, allowing them to become the experts on their own nutritional requirements in order to achieve the long-term goals they seek.

Dana also has a passion for creating quick and easy dishes as well as trying new recipes and sharing them with her clients. She further supports her clients with step-by-step food preparation and grocery shopping tips on social media at facebook.com/rebeldiets.

Dana appears monthly on local Maryland television stations to share REBELLIOUS nutrition tips. She also speaks at conferences across the country and offers seminars and webinars to spread the REBEL message to the public and other health care professionals. She is co-author of *Welcome to the REBELution: 7 Steps to the Nutrition Counseling Practice of Your Dreams*, a guide to help registered dietitians make a career out of doing what they love.

Dana is a member of the *Association for Size Diversity and Health*. She is a board member of *Behavioral Health Nutrition, a dietetic practice group of the Academy of Nutrition and Dietetics*, and a member of the *Nutrition Entrepreneurs, a dietetic practice group of the Academy of Nutrition and Dietetics*.

REBECCA BITZER, MS, RD, LD, CEDRD

Rebecca is an award-winning registered dietitian who is both a seasoned nutrition counselor and successful business owner of Rebecca Bitzer & Associates: The Nutrition Experts, Inc. Rebecca employs 13 staff members including six registered dietitians with offices in Greenbelt and Columbia, MD. She has been passionate about helping clients overcome their eating issues for over twenty-five years. As a registered dietitian and Certified Eating Disorder Registered Dietitian, she has the knowledge and experience to provide both individual and group nutrition counseling to clients of all ages and backgrounds.

She enjoys finding creative solutions that keep her clients motivated to make positive lifestyle changes while meeting their nutrition goals. She strives to continually fine-tune her nutrition counseling skills, sharpen her knowledge of dietetics, and develop new programs to encourage the success of her clients.

Rebecca pioneered the collection of Empowered Eating programs including the *REBEL Against Dieting* program which is designed to provide education, personalized care, and insight into a healthy, happy life that does not include dieting. The REBEL approach includes breaking out of dieting prison, eating mindfully, and reclaiming a rich and meaningful life. REBEL clients overcome their food and weight struggles with the help of her team of registered dietitians using the skills and information in this workbook.

She is a leader in her field and enjoys giving back to the profession of dietetics by serving as Private Practice Chair of *Nutrition Entrepreneurs, a dietetic practice group of the Academy of Nutrition and Dietetics*, and as the coordinator of *Ask the Doc* for the *Disordered Eating and Eating Disorders, a sub-unit of the Sports, Cardiovascular, and Wellness Nutrition, a dietetic practice group of the Academy of Nutrition and Dietetics.*

Rebecca is coauthor of *Welcome to the REBELution: 7 Steps to the Nutrition Counseling Practice of Your Dreams*, a guide to help registered dietitians make a career out of doing what they love.

Rebecca speaks nationally about the Empowered Eating *REBEL Against Dieting* program and was recently awarded *Behavioral Health and Nutrition*'s Excellence in Practice in Eating Disorders award and *Today's Dietitian* magazine's Sixth Annual Showcase of 10 Incredible RDs Who Are Making a Difference.

About Empowered Eating

Our Mission

The mission of Empowered Eating is to provide freedom from food struggles and hope for people and their loved ones challenged with eating disorders. We help clients learn the skills they need to break free from the stress of eating so they can transform their lives.

How We Work

We work closely with physicians, therapists, and other fitness and health professionals in the area to provide the most comprehensive care for our clients. As of this writing we provide nutrition counseling for 7,000 client appointments per year. Our expertise includes programs and services for eating disorders, weight management, wellness, diabetes, heart health, digestive difficulties, sports nutrition, pediatrics, PCOS, and women's health.

How We Give Back

Empowered Eating is passionate about giving back to the profession of dietetics, including hiring dietetic interns and nutrition students. Our registered dietitians are active in the *Academy of Nutrition and Dietetics* and a variety of its dietetic practice groups including *Nutrition Entrepreneurs, Behavioral Health Nutrition, and Sports, Cardiovascular, and Wellness Nutrition*. We also lead speaking events, fundraisers, and community outreach to provide opportunities for dietetics students in order to further growth in the field. We are active on social media, broadening our reach to thousands of readers each day with the goal of changing the conversation to positive self-talk and debunking nutrition myths.

What We Can Do for You

The Empowered Eating team combines expert nutrition advice with the kind hearts of our providers. Our primary goal is to empower individuals to live a fulfilling and healthy life.

Contact Us

> ## REBEL Dietitian® Team
>
> Kait Fortunato Greenberg, RD, LD
>
> Dana Magee, RD, LD
>
> Rebecca Bitzer, CEO, MS, RD, CEDRD
>
> Phone: 301-474-2499 * Fax: 301-474-5943
>
> 7219 D. Hanover Parkway, Greenbelt, MD 20770
>
> E-mail: admin@empoweredeatingblog.com

References

Anderson J, et al. Long-term weight-loss maintenance: a meta-analysis of US studies. *Am J Clin Nutr*. 2001; 74(5): 579-584.

Bacon L. *Health at Every Size, The Surprising Truth About Your Weight*. Dallas, TX: BenBella Books, Inc.; 2013.

Birch LL, Fisher JO. Development of eating behaviors among children and adolescents. *Pediatrics*.1998; 101(3 pt 2): 539–549.

Bishop J, et al. Childhood Obesity. *US Department of Health and Human Services: Office of the Assistant Secretary for Planning and Evaluation*. August 2005. http://aspe.hhs.gov/health/reports/child_obesity/. Accessed June 1, 2015.

Bouchard C. Genetic Determinants of Regional Fat Distribution. Human Reproduction: *Oxford Journals*. 1997; 12(1): 1-5.

Brown R, Ogden J. Children's eating attitudes and behaviour: a study of the modelling and control theories of parental influence. *Oxford Journal- Health Education Research*. 2004;19(3): 261-71.

National Cancer Institute. NCI Funding Policy for RPG Awards FY15. http://deainfo.nci.nih.gov/grantspolicies/FinalFundLtr.htm Accessed June 1, 2015.

Chilton FH, Tucker L. *Win the War Within*. Jackson, TN :Perseus Books Group; 2006.

Choquet H, Meyre D. Genetics of obesity: What have we learned? *Curr Genomics*. 2011;12(3): 169-179.

Clifford D, et al. Impact of non-diet approaches on attitudes, behaviors, and health outcomes: A systematic review. *Journal of Nutrition Education and Behavior*. 2015; 47(2): 143-155.

Costin C. *Your Dieting Daughter...Is She Dying for Attention?* New York, NY: Brunner/Mazel Inc; 1997.

Costin C, Grabb GS. *8 Keys to Recovery from an Eating Disorder*. New York, NY: W. W. Norton & Company; 2012.

Cuddy A. Your Body Language Shapes Who You Are. TED. http://www.ted.com/talks/amy_cuddy_your_body_language_shapes_who_you_are?language=en. June 2012. Accessed June 1, 2015.

Dalzell H. Pathological dieting: Precursor to eating disorders. Examiner. July 14, 2010. http://www.examiner.com/article/pathological-dieting-precursor-to-eating-disorders. Accessed June 1, 2015.

Deal B, Sumner B. *Savvy Girl, A Guide to Eating.* USA: Savvy Girl; 2014.

Dietz, Lisa. Behavior Chain Analysis. DBT Self-Help. http://dbtselfhelp.com/html/behavior_chain_analysis.html. 2012. Accessed June 1, 2015.

Do R, Bailey SD, Desbiens K, et al. Genetic variants of FTO influence adiposity, insulin sensitivity, leptin levels, and resting metabolic rate in the Quebec Family Study. *Diabetes.* 2008;57(4): 1147-50.

Dubois L, Ohm Kyvik K, Girard M, et al. Genetic and environmental contributions to weight, height, and BMI from birth to 19 years of age: An international study of over 12,000 twin pairs. *PLoS ONE.* 2012; 7(2): e30153.

Eating Disorders: Critical Points for Early Recognition and Medical Risk Management in the Care of Individuals with Eating Disorders. *Academy of Eating Disorders*; 2012.

Engeln R. 'The Problem with Fat Talk.' The New York Times, 2015.

Feeding and Eating Disorders. Diagnostic and Statistical Manual of Mental Disorders (DSM-5). *American Psychiatric Publishing*; 2013.

Field AE. Relation between dieting and weight change among preadolescents and adolescents. *Pediatrics.* 2003;112(4): 900-906.

Fisher JO, Birch LL. Restricting access to palatable foods affects children's behavioral response, food selection, and intake. *Am J Clin Nutr.* 1999; 69(6):1264- 1272.

Fletcher M. Different Types of Hunger. The Center for Mindful Eating. http://www.thecenterformindfuleating.org/Resources/Documents/ADifferentTypesofHungerHandout.pdf. March 23, 2010. Accessed: June 1, 2015.

Franz M. Protein controversies in diabetes. *Diabetes Spectrum.* 2000;13(3): 132.

Gaesser GA. *Big Fat Lies: The Truth About Your Weight and Your Health.* Carlsbad, CA: Gurze Books; 2002.

Goodwin J. Rate of eating disorders in kids keeps rising. Health Day. http://consumer.healthday.com/mental-health-information-25/anorexia-news-28/rate-of-eating-disorders-in-kids-keeps-rising-646574.html. November 29, 2010. Accessed: June 1, 2015.

Green Mountain at Fox Run. www.fitwoman.com. ©1997-201. Accessed: June 1, 2015.

Guelinckx I, Klein A, Perreir E, Metzger D, Pross N. Changes in daily water intake impact mood of high and low drinkers. *The FASEB Journal*. 2013; 27:840.11

Hai Liu R. Nutrient, food, and dietary patterns. Health benefits of fruit and vegetables are from additive and synergistic combinations of phytochemicals. *Am J Clin Nutr*. 2003; 78(3): 517S-520S.

Harris, R. *The Happiness Trap: How to Stop Struggling and Start Living*. Boston, MA: Trumpeter; 2008.

How will eating together benefit your family? PA Nutrition Education Network. http://www.panen.org/eattogetherpa/whyfamilymeals. Accessed: June 1, 2015.

Kalm LM, Semba RD. They starved so that others be better fed: Remembering Ancel Keys and the Minnesota Experiment. *The Journal of Nutrition*. 1005; 135(6): 1347-1352.

Kater K, Rohwer J, Londre K. Evaluation of an upper elementary school program to prevent body image, eating and weight concerns. *Journal of School Health*. 2002; 72(5): 199-204.

Knutson KL, Spiegel K, Penev P, Van Cauter E. The metabolic consequences of sleep deprivation. *NIPHA*. 2007; 11(3): 163-178.

Kravitz L, Cazares A, Mermier C. Women, hormones, metabolism and energy expenditure, *IDEA Fitness Journal*. 2013; 10(7): 56-64.

Locke AE, Kahali B, Berndt SI, et al. Genetic studies of body mass index yield new insights for obesity biology. *Nature*. 2015; 518(7538): 197-206.

Maes H, Neale MC, Eaves LJ. Genetic and environmental factors in relative body weight and human adiposity. *Behavior Genetics*. 1997; 27(4): 325-326.

Mann T. Medicare's search for effective obesity treatments: Diets are not the answer. *American Psychological Association*. 2007;62(3): 220–233.

Matz J, Frankel E. *Beyond a Shadow of a Diet: The Comprehensive Guide to Treating Binge Eating Disorder, Compulsive Eating, and Emotional Overeating*. New York, NY: Routledge; 2014.

Matz J, Frankel E. *Beyond a Shadow of a Diet, The Therapist's Guide to Treating Compulsive Eating Disorders*. New York, NY: Routledge; 2004.

May M. *Eat What You Love, Love What You Eat, How to Break Your Eat-Repent-Repeat Cycle*. Austin, TX: Greenleaf Book Group Press; 2011.

May M. *Eat What You Love, Love What You Eat with Diabetes, A Mindful Eating Program for Thriving with Prediabetes Or Diabetes*. Oakland, CA: New Harbinger Publications Incorporated; 2012.

Mazzeo SE, Bulik CM. Environmental and genetic risk factors for eating disorders: What the clinician needs to know. *Child and Adolescent Psychiatric Clinics of North America*. 2009;18 (1):67-82. doi:10.1016/j.chc.2008.07.003.

National Association of Eating Disorders. www.nationaleatingdisorders.org/index.php. 2011. Accessed June 1, 2015.

National Cancer Institute. Cancer Research Funding. http://www.cancer.gov/cancertopics/factsheet/NCI/research-funding, 2014.

National Institutes of Health Office of Dietary Supplements. *Calcium*. http://ods.od.nih.gov/factsheets/Calcium-HealthProfessional/#h3. Accessed June 1, 2015

Neumark-Sztainer D, et al. Dieting and disordered eating behaviors from adolescence to young adulthood: Findings from a 10-year longitudinal study. *Journal of the American Dietetic Association*. 2011;111(7):1004-1011.

Neumark-Sztainer D, et al. Family weight talk and dieting: How much do they matter for body dissatisfaction and disordered eating behaviors in adolescent girls? *The Journal of adolescent health : official publication of the Society for Adolescent Medicine*. 2010;47(3):270-276.

Neumark-Sztainer D. et al. Obesity, disordered eating, and eating disorders in a longitudinal study of adolescents: how do dieters fare five years later? *J Am Diet Assoc*. 2006; 106(4): 559-568.

O'Dea J, Abraham S. Improving the body image, eating attitudes, and behaviors of young male and female adolescents: A new educational approach that focuses on self-esteem. *International Journal of Eating Disorders*. 2000; 28: 43-57.

Oliver G, Wardle J. Perceived effects of stress on food choice. *Physiology and Behavior*. 1999; 6(3): 511-515.

Osterweil N. The Benefits of Protein. WebMD. http://www.webmd.com/men/features/benefits-protein. 2004. Accessed: June 1, 2015.

Pershing A. Do No Harm: Essential Considerations in the Treatment of BED. [PPT]. Binge Eating Disorder Association. 2014.

Pietilainen KH, et al. Does dieting make you fat? A twin study. *International Journal of Obesity*. 2011; 36(3): 456-64.

Redman LM, et al. Metabolic and behavioral compensations in response to caloric restriction: implications for the maintenance of weight loss. *PLoS ONE*. 2009; 4(2): e4377.

Robison J. Helping without harming: kids, eating, weight and health. *Absolute Advantage*. 2007; 7(1): 1-15, 30, 31.

Romanick N. "After the Binge" Webinar. Rosewood Centers for Eating Disorders. 2015.

Ross CC. *The Binge Eating & Compulsive Overeating Workbook, An Integrated Approach to Overcoming Disordered Eating*. Oakland, CA: New Harbinger Publications Incorporated; 2009.

Satter E. Division of Responsibility in Feeding. Ellyn Satter Institute. http://ellynsatterinstitute.org/dor/divisionofresponsibilityinfeeding.php. 2015. Accessed: June 1, 2015.

Satter E. *Secrets of Feeding a Healthy Family, How to Eat, How to Raise Good Eaters, How to Cook*. Madison, WI: Kelcy Press; 2008.

Schaefer J, Magnunson A. A review of interventions that promote eating by internal cues. *Journal of the Academy of Nutrition and Dietetics*. 2014; 114(5): 634-760.

Schott C, Stenovec L. Taking the focus off weight in the dietetics profession: A path for new RDN's. *BHNewsletter*. 2015; 32(3): 10-11.

Shadix K. Reducing Sodium in Canned Beans — Easier Than 1-2-3. *Today's Dietitian*. 2010; 12(1): 62.

Stevens V, Jacobs E, Sun J, Patel A, et al. Weight cycling and mortality in large prospective US study. *Am J Epidemiol*. 2012; 175(8): 785-792.

St-Onge MP. The Role of Sleep Duration in the Regulation of Energy Balance: Effects on Energy Intakes and Expenditure. *Journal of Clinical Sleep Medicine*. 2013; 9(1): 73–80.

Strohacker K, Carpenter KC, McFarlin BK. Consequences of weight cycling: an increase in disease risk? *Int J Exerc Sci*. 2009; 2(3): 191–201.

Stunkard AJ, Harris JR, Pedersen N, McClearn G. The body-mass index of twins who have been reared apart. *N Engl J Med*. 1990; 322: 1483-1487.

Sumithran P, Proietto J. The defence of body weight: a physiological basis for weight regain after weight loss. *Journal of Clinical Science*. 2013; 124(4): 231-241.

Tribole E, Resch E. *Intuitive Eating: A Revolutionary Program that Works*. New York, NY: St. Martin's Paperbacks; 1996.

Wagner R, Machiacao F, Fritsche A, Stefan N, Haring HU, Staiger H. The genetic influence on body fat distribution. *Drug Discover Today: Disease Mechanisms.* 2013; 10(1-2): e5-e13.

Walley AJ, Blakemore A, Froguel P. Genetics of obesity and the prediction of risk for health. *Human Molecular Genetics.* 2006; 15(2): R124-R130.

Wansink B. *Mindless Eating, Why We Eat More Than We Think.* New York, NY: Bantam; 2010.

Wansink B, Chandon P. Can 'low-fat' nutrition labels lead to obesity? *Journal of Marketing Research.* 2006; 43(4): 605-617.

Weighing the claims in diet ads. Federal Trade Commission. http://www.consumer.ftc.gov/articles/0061-weighing-claims-diet-ads. July 2012. Accessed: June 1, 2015.

Yaemsiri S, Slining M M, Agarwal S K. Perceived weight status, overweight diagnosis, and weight control among US adults: the NHANES 2003–2008 Study. *International Journal of Obesity.* 2011; 35(8): 1063-1070.

Heat relaxes muscles
    └ patches, warm shower, towel

Cold reduces swelling
    ┌ ice cubles = bag, froze veggies = Towel
    └ 20 min.